CAMBRIDGE NATIONAL

LEVEL 1/2

Sport Science

Mike Murray & Ross Howitt

An OCR endorsed textbook

The Publishers would like to thank the following for permission to reproduce copyright material.

p.153 © Crown Copyright. Public Health England in association with the Welsh government, the Scottish government and the Food Standards Agency in Northern Ireland.

Photo credits
p.1 © IMAGEMORE Co.,Ltd./Getty Images; **p.3** t © Jürgen Keßler/Dpa picture alliance/Alamy Stock Photo, c © MrPreecha/stock.adobe.com, b © Brenda Carson/stock.adobe.com; **p.4** © Alex/stock.adobe.com; **p.5** © Anawhite1/stock.adobe.com; **p.6** © polhansen/stock.adobe.com; **p.8** © Antonio Ciufo/Alamy Stock Photo; **p.10** t © Concept w/stock.adobe.com, b © SAM YEH/AFP/Getty Images; **p.11** © Kaneos Media/Shutterstock.com; **p.12** t © Simonkr/E+/Getty Images, b © Africa Studio/stock.adobe.com; **p.16** © PointImages/stock.adobe.com; **p.17** © Jules Frazier/Photodisc/Getty Images; **p.18** © Mike Booth/Alamy Stock Photo; **p.19** © Hero Images/Getty Images; **p.22** © Martin81/Shutterstock; **p.23** © Syda Productions/stock.adobe.com; **p.25** t © Adam Burn/fStop Images GmbH/Alamy Stock Photo, b © Kimberly Reinick/stock.adobe.com; **p.26** l © Dreamsquares/stock.adobe.com, r © Photographee.eu/stock.adobe.com; **p.35** © Vectorfusionart/stock.adobe.com; **p.37** © Vadimdem/stock.adobe.com; **p.38** l © Monkey Business/stock.adobe.com, c © Simon/stock.adobe.com, r © Asferico/stock.adobe.com; **p.42** © Master1305/stock.adobe.com; **p.43** t © Sam74100 – 123RF, b © Pressmaster/stock.adobe.com; **p.44** t © ALAN EDWARDS/Alamy Stock Photo, b © Dominique Douieb/PhotoAlto/Alamy Stock Photo; **p.45** © Klaus Vedfelt/DigitalVision/Getty Images; **p.46** © Arttim/stock.adobe.com; **p.47** l © Tetra Images/Getty Images, r © monkeybusiness/iStock/Thinkstock; **p.50** © LMproduction/stock.adobe.com; **p.51** l © Artem Varnitsin/stock.adobe.com, tr © Martin Novak/123RF.com, br © Dušan Zidar/stock.adobe.com; **p.52** © Vakkerartem/stock.adobe.com; **p.56** © Sputnik/Topfoto.co.uk; **p.59** t © Studioloco/stock.adobe.com, b © Deagreez/stock.adobe.com; **p.61** © Dudley Little/Alamy Stock Photo; **p.66** © Bojan/stock.adobe.com; **p.74** © WavebreakMediaMicr/stock.adobe.com; **p.75** t © Pressmaster/stock.adobe.com, c © Pressmaster/stock.adobe.com, b © Jale Ibrak/stock.adobe.com; **p.79** © Wavebreakmedia Ltd/Thinkstock/Getty Images; **p.93** © Bevisphoto/stock.adobe.com; **p.94** © JGI/Jamie Grill/Tetra Images, LLC/Alamy Stock Photo; **p.97** © Dotshock/123RF; **p.98** © iStock/Thinkstock/Getty Images; **p.102** © ExQuisine – Fotolia; **p.116** t © Glisic_albina/stock.adobe.com, b © Wavebreakmedia Ltd/Thinkstock/Getty Images; **p.119** © Chip Simons/Stockbyte/Getty Images; **p.123** l © Carlos Caetano/stock.adobe.com, r © Wavebreak Media Ltd/123RF.com; **p.125** © WILLIAM WEST/AFP/Getty Images; **p.128** © Mnirat/stock.adobe.com; **p.129** © ALLSTAR Picture Library/Alamy Stock Photo; **p.130** © Warren Goldswain/iStock/Thinkstock/Getty Images; **p.133** t © Massimhokuto/stock.adobe.com, b © Rena Schild/Shutterstock.com; **p.136** © Alex Livesey/Getty Images Sport/Getty Images; **p.142** © Phil Oldham/REX/Shutterstock; **p.147** © LIGHTFIELD STUDIOS/stock.adobe.com; **p.148** © Microgen/stock.adobe.com; **p.151** © Milosducati/stock.adobe.com; **p.159** © Bit24/stock.adobe.com; **p.160** t © Anaumenko/stock.adobe.com, c © BillionPhotos.com/stock.adobe.com, b © R. Gino Santa Maria/stock.adobe.com; **p.163** © Helder Almeida/stock.adobe.com; **p.165** t © Nenetus/stock.adobe.com, b © SolStock/E+/Getty Images; **p.167** t © Colin Edwards – Fotolia.com, c © Maksym Yemelyanov/stock.adobe.com, b © Pictooores/stock.adobe.com; **p.181** © Sergey Nivens/stock.adobe.com; **p.183** © Matt/stock.adobe.com; **p.184** © Shariff Che'Lah/stock.adobe.com; **p.189** t © Yiorgos GR/Shutterstock.com; **p.194** © Olly/stock.adobe.com; **p.195** t © Duif du Toit/Gallo Images Sport/Getty Images, b © Ed van de Pol/Soccrates/Getty Images Sport/Getty Images; **p.198** © GABRIEL BOUYS/AFP/Getty Images; **p.201** © SWpix/British Cycling; **p.202** t © Neil Tingle/Alamy Stock Photo, b © Visionhaus/Getty Images Sport/Getty Images; **p.203** © Ross Kinnaird/ALLSPORT/Getty Images Sport/Getty Images; **p.204** © Anthony Au-Yeung/Stringer/Getty Images Sport/Getty Images.

Every effort has been made to trace all copyright holders, but if any have been inadvertently overlooked, the Publishers will be pleased to make the necessary arrangements at the first opportunity.

Orders: please contact Bookpoint Ltd, 130 Park Drive, Milton Park, Abingdon, Oxon OX14 4SE. Telephone: +44 (0)1235 827827. Fax: +44 (0)1235 400401. Email: education@bookpoint.co.uk Lines are open from 9 a.m. to 5 p.m., Monday to Saturday, with a 24-hour message answering service. You can also order through our website: www.hoddereducation.co.uk

ISBN: 978 1 5104 5643 3

© Mike Murray, Ross Howitt 2019
First published in 2019 by
Hodder Education,
An Hachette UK Company
Carmelite House
50 Victoria Embankment
London EC4Y 0DZ

www.hoddereducation.co.uk

Impression number   10 9 8 7 6 5 4 3 2

Year   2023 2022 2021 2020 2019

Cover photo © Sebastian Kaulitzki – stock.adobe.com

Illustrations by Aptara Inc.

Typeset in India by Aptara Inc.

Printed in Italy by Printer Trento S.r.l.

A catalogue record for this title is available from the British Library.

The teaching content of this resource is endorsed by OCR for use with specification Cambridge Nationals Level 1/2 in Sport Science (J812). In order to gain OCR endorsement, this resource has been reviewed against OCR's endorsement criteria.

This resource was designed using the most up to date information from the specification. Specifications are updated over time which means there may be contradictions between the resource and the specification, therefore please use the information on the latest specification and Sample Assessment Materials at all times when ensuring students are fully prepared for their assessments.

Any references to assessment and/or assessment preparation are the publisher's interpretation of the specification requirements and are not endorsed by OCR. OCR recommends that teachers consider using a range of teaching and learning resources in preparing learners for assessment, based on their own professional judgement for their students' needs. OCR has not paid for the production of this resource, nor does OCR receive any royalties from its sale. For more information about the endorsement process, please visit the OCR website, www.ocr.org.uk.

FSC
www.fsc.org

MIX
Paper from
responsible sources
FSC™ C104740

Contents

Acknowledgements

Table 2.4 Burpees completed over five minutes comparison chart from www.spartancoaches.com/spartan-group-exercise-fitness-test.php. Reprinted with permission of Spartan Race, Inc.; **Table 2.5** Squat Test Table adapted from *Total Fitness for Men*, an eBook by Vincent Antonetti, Phd, published by NoPaperPress LLC; **Table 2.6** https://www.topendsports.com; **Table 2.7** Comparison scores from the vertical jump test from www.topendsports.com/ testing/tests/home-vertical-jump.htm. Reprinted with permission of Topend Sports Network; **Table 2.8** Comparative scoring table for the long jump test from www.topendsports.com/testing/tests/longjump.htm. Reprinted with permission of Topend Sports Network; **Table 2.9** Davis B. et al; *Physical Education and the Study of Sport* © Elsevier 2000; **Table 2.11** Comparison scores for the sit-and-reach test. Data supplied by Top End Sports www. topendsports.com. Reprinted with permission of Topend Sports Network; **Table 2.12** Davis B. et al; *Physical Education and the Study of Sport* © Elsevier 2000; **Table 2.14** Normative data for the Harvard step test for 16 year olds from Beashel, P and Taylor, J (1997) 'Fitness for Health and performance'. In: Beashel, P and Taylor, J, *The World of Sport Examined*. Croatia: Thomas Nelson and Sons, p.55; **Table 2.15** Bizley, K. et al. (2010) *BTEC First Sport Level 2*, London, HarperCollins Publishers Limited. Reprinted by permission of HarperCollins Publishers Ltd © 2010; **Figure 4.21** *Literature reviews in sport psychology* by Mellalieu, Stephen D.; Hanton, Sheldon Reproduced with permission of Nova Science Publishers in the format Book via Copyright Clearance Center; **Figure 4.22** SCAT questions from *Sport Competition Anxiety Test*, Rainer Martens, 1980 © Human Kinetics. Reprinted with permission.

How to use this book

Key features of the book

Learning outcomes

LO1 Understand different factors which influence the risk of injury

LO2 Understand how appropriate warm up and cool down routines can help to prevent injury

Prepare for what you are going to cover in the unit.

How will I be assessed?

You will be assessed through a one-hour written paper, set and marked by OCR, that is worth 50 per cent of your overall mark for the OCR Level 1/2 Cambridge National Award in Sport Science, or 25 per cent of the overall mark

Understand all the requirements of the new qualification fully with clearly stated learning outcomes and what you will be assessed on for each learning outcome, fully matched to the specification.

Links to other units

You can find further information on this topic in Unit R044.

Relevant links to other units and learning outcomes.

Key terms

Power Exerting muscular strength rapidly.

Agility The ability to move and change direction quickly while maintaining control.

Understand important terms.

Getting started

Many factors (things) can cause injury in sport. Working with a partner, choose a sport and list some of the factors that could cause injury in that particular sport.

Short activity to introduce you to the topic.

Classroom discussion

Discuss the physical and psychological benefits of completing a suitable warm up.

Discuss topics with others and test your understanding.

Stretch activity

On the storyboard produced by your group, add details that explain the physical benefits of these cool down activities.

Take your understanding and knowledge of a topic a step further with these stretch activities designed to test you, and provide you with a more in depth understanding of the topic.

Group activity

Using the list created in the getting started exercise, identify whether the activities have physical or psychological benefits.

Work in groups to discuss and reflect on topics, and share ideas.

Know it!

1 Explain the physical aspects of a warm up and cool down.
2 Describe a range of warm up and cool down techniques and activities, and the areas of the body that they target.

Test your understanding with this end of unit task.

Assessment preparation

Think about the tasks that your teacher may set you to assess your knowledge of the principles of training. Make sure you:

● know what the principles of training are and can relate them to different activities
● are clear about what is meant by:
  ○ progressive overload
  ○ specificity
  ○ reversibility/regression
  ○ moderation
  ○ variance.

Guidance and suggestions on what you will need to cover for the OCR model assignment and a breakdown of what the command words mean.

Read about it

Causes of sports injuries:
www.health24.com/Medical/Sports-injuries/Overview/causes-of-sports-injuries-20160329

Includes references to books, websites and other various sources for further reading and research.

R041 Reducing the risk of sports injuries

About this unit

People working in the sport and leisure industries need to be aware of the possibility of injury through involvement in sport and physical activity. Knowing how to reduce the risk of injury when taking part in sport, and how to respond to injuries and medical conditions in a sport setting, are important skills.

This unit looks at how to prepare performers for taking part in physical activity so that the risk of injury is minimised. It also describes how to respond to common sports injuries and how to recognise the symptoms of some common medical conditions, providing a solid foundation for those interested in more formal first-aid training and qualifications.

Learning outcomes

LO1 Understand different factors which influence the risk of injury

LO2 Understand how appropriate warm up and cool down routines can help to prevent injury

LO3 Know how to respond to injuries within a sporting context

LO4 Know how to respond to common medical conditions

How will I be assessed?

You will be assessed through a one-hour written paper, set and marked by OCR, that is worth 50 per cent of your overall mark for the OCR Level 1/2 Cambridge National Award in Sport Science, or 25 per cent of the overall mark for the OCR Level 1/2 Cambridge National Certificate in Sport Science. During the external assessment, you will be expected to demonstrate your understanding of this unit through questions that require the skills of analysis and evaluation in particular contexts.

For LO1

You need to have knowledge and understanding of:

- extrinsic factors that can influence the risk of injury
- intrinsic factors that can influence the risk of injury.

For LO2

You need to have knowledge and understanding of:

- physical and psychological benefits of a warm up
- key components of a warm up
- physical benefits of a cool down
- key components of a cool down
- specific needs that a warm up and cool down must consider.

For LO3

You need to have knowledge and understanding of:

- the difference between acute and chronic injuries
- common types of sports injuries and their causes and treatment
- how to respond to and treat common sports injuries
- emergency action plans (EAPs) in a sporting context.

For LO4

You need to have knowledge and understanding of:

- symptoms of asthma, diabetes and epilepsy
- treatments for asthma, diabetes and epilepsy.

LO1 Understand different factors which influence the risk of injury

Extrinsic factors

Extrinsic factors that may cause injuries are those where the risk comes from outside the body. Extrinsic factors include the type of sporting activity undertaken, the standard of coaching/supervision provided, the environment in which the activity takes place, the equipment involved and other safety hazards.

Type of activity

Some sports and activities are more dangerous than others, and therefore more likely to result in injuries. The types of injuries that occur also differ depending on the type of activity. For example, rugby is more dangerous than swimming; you are more likely to get injured playing rugby than you are swimming, and you will probably suffer different types of injuries in rugby (e.g. dislocated or broken bones) than when swimming (e.g. shoulder pain).

Getting started

Many factors (things) can cause injury in sport. Working with a partner, choose a sport and list some of the factors that could cause injury in that particular sport.

 Key term

Extrinsic factors Risks or factors from outside the body.

Some sports emphasise or actually require physical contact with other performers. These are known as **contact sports**. Sports such as karate and judo are scored on the physical impact the performer has on an opponent, while others, including rugby and football, require tackling of opposition players. These sports are often known as full-contact sports, as the sport cannot be undertaken without contact. Other sports, such as basketball and netball, may have contact, but such contact is against the rules of the game or is accidental and does not form part of the sport.

The contact in contact sports can include impacts with a piece of sporting equipment. For example in hockey and cricket, injuries can be caused by being struck by a hockey stick (e.g. bruise) or a cricket ball (e.g. concussion).

Non-contact sports are those where performers should have no possible means of touching one another, such as swimming and gymnastics, where performers use separate lanes or take turns to perform.

Some sports, such as cycling, may involve racing in a group with other riders. This often results in brushing and bumping into other cyclists. Cyclists try to avoid contact, however, as it leads to crashes and injuries.

Involvement in contact sports such as football makes it more likely that an injury will occur than when taking part in non-contact sports such as gymnastics.

Some sports involve repeating the same movement over and over again. This can also lead to injury, as the same part of the body is being used and taking extreme strains. For example, the repetitive actions in javelin throwing and cricket bowling place severe strain on the performer's arm and shoulder, which can lead to injuries, such as shoulder impingement syndrome in bowlers, where tendons in the shoulder rub against bone or tissue.

Read about it

Causes of sports injuries:

www.health24.com/Medical/Sports-injuries/Overview/causes-of-sports-injuries-20160329

https://medbroadcast.com/condition/getcondition/sports-injuries

Coaching/supervision

Coaches must have the ability to pass on the correct information to the performers they are supervising. If standards of coaching are poor, or the coach teaches **incorrect techniques**, the risk of sports injury occurring is high. For example, a performer could easily suffer an injury to their head or neck if they were shown the wrong technique for a back drop on the trampoline.

Key terms

Contact sports Sports in which physical contact between performers is an accepted part of play.

Non-contact sports Sports where participants compete alternately, or in lanes, so that they are physically separated, or where the rules detail no contact.

Figure 1.1 Rugby is a contact sport

Figure 1.2 Swimming is a non-contact sport

Figure 1.3 Repetitive movements may lead to injuries

Similarly, if a performer is using the wrong technique for landing at each stage of a triple jump, and the coach is unable to recognise the use of incorrect technique, this could lead to an ankle injury due to the uneven landing.

If a coach has poor or **ineffective communication skills**, this too may lead to injury. A coach who cannot explain what is required accurately may allow dangerous situations to develop. For example, if a coach did not explain how to tackle properly in rugby, a performer could easily suffer an injury to their head or neck.

The coach may not know the rules and regulations of the sport or may be unable to explain them properly, which could lead to injury. For example, they may be unable to explain the rules about tackling from behind in football, which may lead to bad tackles and possible injury.

In much the same way, a coach may allow performers to practise activities without strictly **adhering to the rules and regulations** of the sport, which may lead to injuries. For example, canoeists must wear helmets, but if the coach allows practices to take place without the performers wearing helmets, the possibility of injury is increased.

The rules and regulations of sports are designed to help prevent injuries. For example, there are rules about:

- the number of players allowed on a pitch or court, to stop overcrowding and injuries occurring due to people bumping into each other
- foul and dangerous play, such as a late tackle in rugby
- the misuse of equipment, such as lifting the stick high in hockey
- protective equipment that must be worn in some sports, for example wearing gum shields to prevent damage to teeth in boxing and wearing shin pads to prevent bruising and fractures to the lower leg in football
- age groups, for example to ensure that children play against other children of a similar age in rugby
- safe use of equipment and apparatus, for example the correct way to add or remove weights from a bar in weightlifting
- the supervision required for certain sports, for example there must be lifeguards at swimming events

Environmental factors

The **weather** can have a major impact on playing conditions in outdoor sports, and poor playing conditions can increase the potential for injuries. For example, rain can make playing surfaces hazardous in games such as hockey and football, leading to less control of movements and more likelihood of collisions and injuries. Rain or fog also reduce visibility, increasing the risk of collisions (e.g. in cycling).

Links to other units

You can find further information on this topic in this unit, LO3.

Figure 1.4 Poor weather can increase the risk of injury

Very cold or hot weather can lead to injuries. If it is cold, playing surfaces become harder or frozen, increasing the risk of injuries from falling. Very cold weather also increases the risk of **hypothermia**. If it is hot, the playing surface may again become hard, but there is also the risk of sunburn, **heat exhaustion**, **dehydration** and **heatstroke**.

If the weather is windy or there are gales, sports such as sailing, windsurfing and rock climbing become more dangerous, while the occurrence of lightning endangers the personal safety of all performers (e.g. in golf).

Changes in visibility due to bright sunlight or fog could result in a person not seeing clearly when trying to catch a ball, for example in cricket, resulting in an injury.

The weather may make it necessary for performers to change their style of play, which may lead them to make unusual movements that create further risk of injury.

Sometimes, because of the weather but also due to other reasons, **playing surfaces** and/or the surrounding areas may become slippery. Water or a damp patch in or around a badminton court, for example, can cause injury, as the performers may slip on it and hurt their ankles.

Many playing courts or pitches are surrounded by barriers and advertising boards that can cause injury if a performer collides with them. In sports such as basketball or volleyball, it is quite common for substitutes to sit on benches close to the playing area, offering another potential cause of injury through collisions.

Similarly, the presence of foreign objects on the playing surface or the surrounds – such as litter, glass, wet leaves, stones or other sharp objects – can cause injuries, either through slipping on them or through coming into contact with them.

Sports are competitive – you play against the opposition, and many sports involve the presence of teammates – and these **other participants** are potentially injury-causing. In netball, for example, it is quite possible for participants to run into each other accidentally; to commit a contact foul against another player; to not be fully aware of the rules regarding contact; or for the players to be of different abilities, ages or genders, leading to an imbalance and the prospect of collisions.

Equipment

In many sports, performers use specially designed **protective equipment** to help prevent injuries. For example in sports such as hockey and football, the performers are required by the rules of the game to wear shin pads to prevent injuries to the lower leg. When batting and keeping wicket in cricket, the players wear a much larger form of pad to protect their legs from injury.

Other examples of protective equipment include helmets in skiing and cycling, gum shields in boxing and rugby, shoulder pads in rugby, and knee pads in volleyball. Not wearing the appropriate

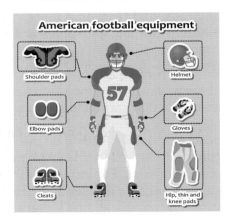

Figure 1.5 Protective equipment

protective equipment, or wearing worn out or ill-fitting protective equipment, is another potential cause of injury (e.g. a split gum shield will not properly protect the teeth of rugby players).

Protective equipment can also be in the form of padding around potentially dangerous objects that are part of the sport. For example, in rugby and volleyball, the posts are heavily padded to prevent collision injuries. In indoor athletics, the ends of the 60 m sprint lanes have protective barriers. In sports such as gymnastics the participants perform on mats to protect them from injuries caused by falling or landing on a hard floor; in trampolining there are protective mats at the edges of the bed.

In many sports, performers make use of equipment that is necessary for **performance**, but it may also have the potential to cause injury. For example, lacrosse and hockey players use sticks, cricketers and lacrosse players throw a hard ball around, and rock climbers and trampolinists may make use of a harness.

When you play a sport, you need to wear suitable **clothing and footwear** for that activity. Clothing and footwear need to be appropriate for the playing surface. Some sports are played on several different surfaces – for example, football may be played on grass, AstroTurf or indoors – and may require the use of different clothing and footwear for the players. Changes in weather conditions also often mean a change to the clothing and type of footwear worn, in order to prevent injury.

In many sports, it is important to wear footwear that is suitable for that particular sport and the circumstances in which the sport is played. For example, football and rugby players wear different types of boots or studs depending on the state of the surface on which they are playing; this gives them more control of their movements and helps to prevent injuries. For instance, AstroTurf football boots have different studs than boots designed for grass. Athletes wear spikes when sprinting, and basketball players wear high-ankle boots for protection.

Wearing inappropriate clothing can cause injury, for example by snagging on the equipment of other performers or by restricting movement. Inappropriate footwear could result in injury through slipping, through not fitting properly. Injury may also be caused through contact with other people's studs or spikes.

Safety hazards

It is important that the people involved in sport – coaches, performers and support staff – are aware of the safety **hazards** and levels of **risk** associated with that sport. It is essential that various health and safety considerations are applied to all activities, prior to and during participation.

In preparation for involvement in sport, a competent person should undertake a **risk assessment**. A competent person is someone with experience, qualifications and expert knowledge of sport safety.

Figure 1.6 Gymnastics uses protective equipment and flooring

 Group activity

Choose three diverse sports and research the protective equipment required for each of them to help prevent injury.

Stretch activity

For each piece of equipment identified in the group activity, explain whether the injury was caused by an intrinsic or extrinsic factor.

Key terms

Hazard Something that can cause harm.

Risk The likelihood of a hazard causing harm.

Risk assessment Careful examination of what, in relation to a sports activity, could cause harm to people and trying to minimise the risk of harm occurring.

A risk assessment identifies the potential hazards of the activity and, in doing so, helps you to plan an alternative safer sports activity if it is too dangerous. A risk assessment also identifies who might be potentially harmed and decides what needs to be done to minimise or eliminate risks so that people don't get hurt. The risk assessment identifies potential hazards and categorises them as low, medium or high. If risks are medium or high, then a decision must be made as to whether the activity is safe enough to go ahead.

Risk assessments help to reduce the potential for injury by assessing the possibilities of an accident happening before the activity takes place. For example in football, the referee should inspect the pitch and decide to call off the game if the pitch is too frozen. The risk assessment suggests actions that need to be taken to reduce the chances of accidents happening. Risk assessments can take place during a match or game too, for example removing litter from a basketball court or stopping the rugby match because of heavy rain making the conditions dangerous.

The risk assessment identifies what facilities or equipment need to be checked before the activity. For example, a rugby referee must check the presence and integrity of the protective padding around the goalposts and make sure that it is securely fastened and will not fall off. A netball umpire must check that the players are not wearing jewellery to prevent potential injuries. The risk assessment will also be concerned with the areas surrounding the pitch or court, such as the presence of advertising hoardings that may be so close to the side of the pitch that the players could run into them.

The risk assessment is not just about the participants. It will also identify any safety concerns for spectators, such as seating arrangements and standing areas for fans in a football stadium.

 Classroom discussion

Look at the list of potential injuries that you identified for a particular sport in the getting started activity. Add any extrinsic factors that may need to be considered to help prevent these injuries.

 Group activity

Working in groups, select a sport and create a poster that identifies the different types of extrinsic factors that can cause injury in that sport.

Stretch activity

Add information to the poster created in the group activity that offers advice on how to reduce these extrinsic risks.

Read about it

Risk assessments:

www.sportenglandclubmatters.com/club-planning/governance/managing-risk-2/risk-assesment

www.sportrisk.com/six-steps-to-sport-clubs-risk-assessment

Risk Assessment

Potential hazard	Who is at risk?	Existing control measures	Risk rating	Preventative measures	Responsibilities

Figure 1.7 A typical risk assessment template

Safety checks are an integral part of risk assessments, as they can identify potential hazards. For example, it is important to safety check the playing area. Finding out that it is uneven or slippery could increase the risk of a performer falling and getting injured. The presence of other people or animals in the playing area, or the playing area being too small, could mean that people get in the way of each other and possibly collide. Other activities could be taking place quite close to the playing area, which increases the chance of being hit by a ball or object from another group or colliding with another person.

The presence of various objects on the playing surface, such as litter, glass, debris, animal faeces or wet leaves, can result in things like cuts, injury or illness to a performer. The environment surrounding the playing area should also be checked, because objects such as trees, fences and advertising banners could potentially cause injury if performers collide with them. Likewise, items such as goal posts, corner posts and other equipment integral to the activity need to be checked to make sure they are secure, in good working order and, if necessary, covered to ensure safety. For example, if rugby posts are not padded, a player could easily run into one and suffer a serious head injury. Similarly, the possibility of a discus leaving the hand of a thrower and causing injury would be reduced if there was netting to stop that happening.

Performers should be checked to make sure they are wearing suitable clothing and/or footwear. They should also be checked for jewellery, which should be removed and/or covered up and protected (e.g. in football, before a substitute can enter the game). Long hair may need to be tied back in some activities and, in sports such as netball, fingernail length needs to be checked to prevent scratches.

In activities such as fitness sessions, those taking part should be checked to make sure that they are fit enough to perform at the required level, and that the instructor is made aware of any previous injuries or health issues (e.g. in an induction session at a gym).

Injuries can occur at any time and during any sporting activity. The coaches, staff and volunteers involved in the activity must be prepared and ready to face emergency situations. This preparation involves the development of an **emergency action plan (EAP)**. An EAP is a written plan of what action to take in the event of an emergency at a sporting event. More details are given on EAPs in Learning Outcome 3, pages 27–28.

Intrinsic factors

Intrinsic factors are those that come from within your own body. Intrinsic factors that may cause injury in sporting activities include the physical preparation for the activity, any individual variables between performers, psychological factors, posture and the causes of poor posture, and sports injuries related to poor posture.

Figure 1.8 Objects surrounding the court may be potential safety hazards.

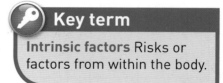
Key term

Intrinsic factors Risks or factors from within the body.

Read about it

Intrinsic risk factors:

https://asaxoninjuries.wordpress.com/intrinsic-risk-factors

https://wanstall96.wordpress.com/intrinsic-risk-factors-2

Physical preparation

One of the main causes of injury to participants in sporting activities is a lack of physical preparation. In order to undertake sporting activities, performers should prepare by making sure their body is fit enough to withstand the rigours of physical activity. This will involve **training**. A lack of **fitness** caused by a lack of training will expose the performer to a number of intrinsic risks of injury. Tired and tight muscles brought about by fatigue cannot support the skeleton as they are designed to. When fatigued, you tend to sit or stand incorrectly, and tend to slouch.

One important aspect of preparation is a suitable **warm up**. A warm up prevents injury by making sure that the body is ready for physical activity. It involves exercising or practising gently before the activity and prepares the heart, joints and muscles for vigorous actions and also has psychological benefits.

Jogging   Marching   Back kicking   Front kicking   Hands in the air

Foot touching   Knee bending   Ankle holding stretch   Arm, leg and torso stretch

Figure 1.9 Typical warm up exercises

In much the same way as a warm up prepares the body for physical activity, a **cool down** allows the body to shift gradually to a resting or near-resting state. A cool down comprises easy exercises, completed after the training, which can help prevent muscle soreness.

Repeated exercising on a body that is not properly prepared may result in **overuse injuries**. Overuse injuries are caused by repetitive actions, which damage **tendons**, **ligaments**, muscles and soft tissues over a period of time.

In order to move, we need muscles. As a muscle contracts, it shortens; at the same time, its partner on the opposite side lengthens. Sometimes one of these pairs of muscles is stronger than the other, and this can cause **muscle imbalance**. Muscle imbalance can lead to overuse injuries as our bodies try to counteract the imbalance.

Key terms

Training The process of bringing a person to a suitable level of proficiency.

Fitness Set of qualities relating to a person's ability to perform physical activity.

Warm up A simple exercise routine performed before a training session.

Cool down Easy exercise done after more intense exercise to allow the body to recover to resting levels.

Overuse injuries Chronic injuries caused by repetitive movements.

Tendons Attach muscles to bone.

Ligaments Fibrous bands that join bone to bone to strengthen joints.

Muscle imbalance Where one muscle is more powerful than an opposing one.

Links to other units

You can find further information on this topic in this unit, LO2.

Muscle imbalance can be the result of playing sports where one side of the body is used slightly more than the other, as in the repetitive action of hitting a tennis ball right- or left-handed. For a sport where the performer uses one side of their body 60–70 per cent more than the other, such as a rugby player who takes penalty kicks with one foot, training should include using both feet to prevent muscle imbalance. This will not only ensure the body is completely balanced in strength and agility, but will also help them to become a better player.

Muscle imbalance can also result from incorrect weight training, such as performing too many **biceps** curls without strengthening the back of the arms (**triceps**) at the same time. Another common form of muscle imbalance is where people train their upper body and ignore their legs. This can cause weak legs and hips, and a definite imbalance. Screening for muscle imbalance is a good way of preventing injury and is becoming more and more popular.

Individual variables

All people are different – they all have individual variables meaning that what suits one performer may not suit another. One obvious variable is **gender**. What may be suitable for male performers may not be suitable for female performers and vice versa. Trying to perform skills and techniques that are best suited to a particular gender may lead to injury. In general, for example, men tend to be physically stronger than women and therefore women should not be expected to lift the same amount of weight as a male performer. Similarly, women tend to be more flexible than men, and therefore men should be wary of attempting to produce the same range of movements as women.

Another individual variable is **age**. In general, elderly people are not as strong as younger adults. Similarly, young children are not as strong as adults. There is a risk of injury if older people and young children attempt the same strength exercises as young adults.

One of the main components of fitness is **flexibility**. A lack of flexibility will place unnecessary stress on the performer's body during exercise, which may lead to injury. For example, a person who is lacking in flexibility is more likely to **strain** or tear muscles or **sprain** ligaments. A lack of suitable flexibility may cause a performer to use poor technique, which could lead to an injury in the longer term. On the other hand, increased flexibility tends to make you less prone to injuries.

Taking part in physical activity pushes your body to the edge. You make progress and improve your fitness by stressing your body through training and allowing it to recover. Without adequate **nutrition** from your diet, this recovery is not possible.

Key terms

Biceps Muscle at the front of the upper arm, which bends the elbow.

Triceps Muscle at the back of the upper arm, which straightens the elbow.

Flexibility The ability to move joints through a large range of motion; the range of movement around a joint.

Figure 1.10 Men tend to be able to lift heavier weights than women

Figure 1.11 Women tend to be more flexible than men

Poor nutrition can lead to an increased risk of injury in the following ways:

- Exercise requires energy, which comes from the food you eat. Not eating or drinking enough can lead to a lack of suitable **nutrients** in your body and cause fatigue and **dehydration**, allowing performance to deteriorate.
- It can affect concentration and focus, because the brain needs particular nutrients such as iron. A performer may become too easily distracted, which could cause them to use poor technique and, for example, mistime a challenge or tackle in hockey.
- Too much fat in the diet can lead to a performer becoming overweight, which might lead to more injuries due to increased strain on the knees and ankles.
- A lack of **minerals** or **vitamins** could lead to weak bones and/or muscles.

Insufficient **sleep** before exercise increases the risk of injury. Waking up refreshed and alert following a good night's sleep means that a performer can stay focused and achieve success during activity. Fatigue through a lack of sleep can lead to injuries by:

- causing poor decisions to be made, resulting in dangerous play or poor reaction times
- decreasing **motivation**, for example a rugby player might pull out of a tackle
- increasing performer irritability and aggression.

Injuries are, unfortunately, quite common in physical activities, and a history of **previous or reoccurring injuries** increases the intrinsic risk of injury occurring again during future participation. This is mainly because injury recovery involves rest, and rest means losing fitness, so muscles and tendons become weak and lose their strength and flexibility. It is quite common to hear of people who have returned to participation in physical activity only to immediately reinjure themselves.

Psychological factors

Scientific research has shown that various **psychological factors** can affect the frequency of sports injuries. Psychological factors are the mental factors that affect a performer's 'frame of mind' positively or negatively.

Motivation is the drive to do something. A lack of motivation could mean that a performer does not commit themselves wholeheartedly to an activity. When competing at a high level, for example in contact sports such as boxing, this could cause them to become injured because they are not defending themselves properly. Over-motivation, where a performer gets carried away with their involvement and becomes reckless, could result in too much commitment in an activity and increase the potential for injury.

Figure 1.12 Nutrition is important for preventing injuries

🔑 Key terms

Nutrients Substances in food needed for our bodies to function.

Minerals Inorganic substances that assist the body with many of its functions.

Vitamins Organic substances needed for many essential processes in the body.

Psychological factors Mental factors that can affect a performer positively or negatively.

Motivation The drive to do something.

Links to other units

You can find further information on this topic in Unit R045.

Aggression is the physiological and psychological intention to cause harm to others. This could cause a performer to go into a tackle too hard or to break the rules and cause injury to themselves or an opponent. Aggression can cause a lack of control of movements that may result in poor technique and, in turn, result in an injury. Being aggressive in certain sports can cause other players to retaliate and foul or harm an opponent.

Arousal is the physiological and psychological level of activation of a performer, which ranges from being in a coma to high excitement. **Anxiety** is a negative emotional state concerned with feelings of worry and nervousness. If a performer becomes too aroused or stressed, their anxiety will increase and they may be too worried or nervous to perform in a safe way or could cause injury by not tackling properly or not concentrating enough. Over-arousal may also lead to a performer being too committed and becoming aggressive. Under-arousal can lead to injuries through a lack of confidence, where performers may be unable to concentrate, make the wrong decisions or pull out of tackles (e.g. not locking the ankle joint when tackling in football).

Posture and causes of poor posture

Posture is the position in which someone holds their body when standing or sitting. Poor posture can result from certain muscles tightening up or shortening while others lengthen and become weak, which often occurs because your daily activities are fairly repetitive.

Poor posture can result in injury and may be caused by a number of different factors:

- a poor **gait** (how you walk or run) or stance, for example bending your knees when walking or hunching your shoulders when standing up
- learning or being coached into a poor sporting technique
- adopting a **slouching** or slumping sitting position, rather than sitting upright (sometimes the design of a chair makes it uncomfortable to maintain correct posture)
- adopting an uncomfortable sleeping position in bed
- **physical defects**, for example because of muscles weakened around an injured area
- long-standing or genetic back problems
- the position of the unborn baby during pregnancy
- being overweight or obese
- fatigue, as tired muscles are unable to support the skeleton properly
- **emotional factors**, such as having low self-esteem or lack of confidence causing people to slouch or walk with their head looking down
- wearing ill-fitting **clothing or footwear**, e.g. regularly wearing high-heeled shoes
- carrying heavy bags or luggage.

Figure 1.13 Aggression can lead to injuries

🔑 Key terms

Aggression The intention to cause harm to others.

Arousal The physiological and psychological activation level of a performer, ranging from being in a coma to high excitement.

Anxiety A negative emotional state of worry or nervousness.

Posture Position the body is held in.

Gait How people walk or run.

Slouching Standing, moving or sitting in a lazy, drooping way.

Figure 1.14 Slouching

A **lack of exercise** may also affect posture. A reduction in the strength of the **core muscles** means less support for the body. The core of the body is usually considered to be the trunk or torso. Many of the effortless, pain-free movements needed during a normal day are highly dependent on this part of the body. However, the core becomes even more important during physical activity, when movements need to be highly co-ordinated. A lack of core muscular development can result in a tendency to become injured.

Sports injuries related to poor posture

There are several sports injuries related to poor posture that may affect performance.

The way that your **pelvis** (or hips) line up with your **femur** (or thigh bone) can result in poor posture. When a person's pelvis tips forwards, backwards or to the side, more than the normal range, compared to your femur, then their pelvis is slightly misaligned, and the resulting **pelvic tilt** may cause poor posture.

Key terms

Core muscles Muscles of the trunk.

Pelvis Large bone attached to the backbone and forming the hip joint with the legs.

Femur Thigh bone.

Lordosis Excessive forward or inward curving of the lower back.

Links to other units

You can find further information on this topic in Unit R044.

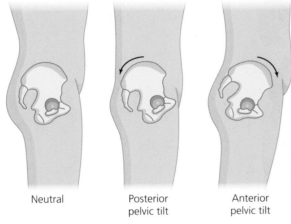

Neutral   Posterior   Anterior
                     pelvic tilt   pelvic tilt

Figure 1.15 Pelvic tilt

Common symptoms of pelvic tilt include pain in the lower back and sometimes in the groin area, stiffness in the morning or after activity, and tightness in the muscles of the lower back and groin region. Pelvic tilt leads other parts of the body to compensate for the misalignment, which can lead to injury.

Lordosis is the name given to a condition in which there is excessive forward or inward curving of the lower back or spine, which gives the appearance of the stomach sticking out. The most common symptom of lordosis is muscle pain. When your spine curves abnormally, your muscles are pulled in different directions, causing them to tighten or spasm, especially the muscles of the lower back. People with lordosis may also suffer from numbness or tingling in their lower back, and weak bladder control.

Ideal posture   Lumbar lordosis

Figure 1.16 Lordosis

Lordosis is a particular problem for gymnasts and dancers. It is also relatively common in overweight men, who tend to carry excess fat in front of the stomach and compensate for this by developing an inward curve of the lower back.

Kyphosis is the name given to the condition where there is excessive backward or outward (convex) curvature of the upper part of the spine or back, so that the upper back appears hunched. People with kyphosis tend to get mild to severe back pain, often linked to movements. They also suffer from tenderness and stiffness in the spine, forward posture of the head and tight hamstrings (the muscles in the back of your thighs).

Cyclists, cricket wicketkeepers and baseball catchers are at risk of developing kyphosis, as they must hold postures with hunched backs for long periods. Weightlifters can also develop kyphosis by overdeveloping and tightening the chest (pectoral) muscles while neglecting the muscles in the upper back.

Key terms

Kyphosis Excessive backward or outward curvature of the upper part of the spine.

Scoliosis Condition where the spine is visibly curved to the side, giving an 'S' or 'C' shape.

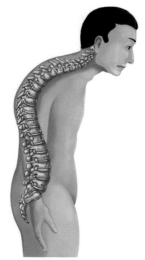

Ideal posture

Round shoulders

Figure 1.17 Kyphosis

Figure 1.18 Round shoulders

An excessive curve forward of the neck that makes the shoulders hunch forward is called **round shoulders**. Common symptoms are a forward head posture, rounded shoulders, a hunched upper back, headaches and shoulder, upper back and neck pain.

Scoliosis is the name of a condition where the spine or backbone is visibly curved to the side, giving an 'S' or 'C' shape, where one shoulder appears higher than the other. People with scoliosis tend to lean to one side and may not be able to stand up straight or bend properly. Often one shoulder blade appears higher or more prominent than the other. They also suffer from back pain.

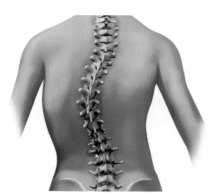

Figure 1.19 Scoliosis

There is some evidence that people who take part in activities that put an uneven load on the spine, for example figure skaters and skiers, may be more susceptible to developing scoliosis. A similar situation occurs when performers take part in activities where emphasis is placed on one side of the body, such as athletic throwing events or racquet sports such as tennis. The continuous imbalance on the spine may lead to the development of scoliosis.

All of the postural misalignments mentioned above can increase the likelihood of injury when playing sport. All lead to muscle imbalance, which can in turn lead to strains or sprains if left untreated. This is why it is important to work both sides of the body. Poor posture can result in poor technique and backache. Postural defects can result in poor balance, which can cause slips and falls. They can also lead to the bones in one part of the body becoming weaker, which increases the risk of stress fractures or the likelihood of injury if you fall.

Stretch activity

Draw stick figures to show the following three conditions related to poor posture: lordosis, kyphosis and scoliosis.

Read about it

Posture:

www.betterhealth.vic.gov.au/health/conditionsandtreatments/posture

Symptoms, causes and treatment of bad posture:

www.thephysiocompany.com/blog/stop-slouching-postural-dysfunction-symptoms-causes-and-treatment-of-bad-posture

Know it!

1 List five extrinsic factors that can influence the risk of injury.
2 List five intrinsic factors that can influence the risk of injury.
3 Sports injuries can be influenced by both extrinsic and intrinsic factors. Which of the following are examples of intrinsic factors?
   a The weather
   b Fitness levels
   c Equipment
   d Age

LO2 Understand how appropriate warm up and cool down routines can help to prevent injury

Physical benefits of a warm up

A warm up is a simple exercise routine that is performed before a workout session or playing sport. It helps to improve the quality of performance and lowers the risk of injury.

A warm up should include:

- physical activity that results in an **increase in body temperature**, so that the muscles become more flexible and there is less chance of injury; this also causes an **increase in heart rate**, which will speed up delivery of oxygen to the working muscles
- some stretching, which **increases the flexibility** of muscles and joints and **the pliability** of ligaments and tendons, to further reduce the chance of injury
- some movement and the release of adrenaline, which will increase blood flow and **speed up delivery of oxygen to the working muscles**, increase the strength and speed of **muscle contractions** and improve reaction time.

A less obvious benefit of a warm up is that there will be a delay in the production of **lactic acid**, which is formed during **anaerobic** exercise, and so fatigue will be delayed and the risk of injury is further reduced.

Read about it

Benefits of warm ups:

http://benefitof.net/benefits-of-warm-up

Warming up and stretching:

www.fitnesshealth101.com/fitness/weight-training/beginners/warm-up

Psychological benefits of a warm up

During a warm up, there is time to think about the activity that is about to be undertaken, allowing the performer to **heighten or control arousal levels**. This is sometimes called 'getting in the zone', which really means being at the ideal level of arousal. For some performers, it allows them to calm down and settle their nerves. Reducing levels of arousal ensures the performer is fully focused on what needs to be done, will use the correct technique and will not make any rash decisions. Being over-aroused can lead to injury, as the performer is too 'wound-up'. Under-arousal may also cause injury, due to being too casual in your approach to the activity, leading to you missing vital cues as to what is happening around you.

Getting started

Most people taking this course are active participants in sport. Working with a partner, write down as many activities that you can remember having done as part of a warm up before an activity and as part of a cool down after an activity.

Figure 1.20 Warming up helps to improve the quality of performance and lowers the risk of injury

Key terms

Heart rate Number of times the heart contracts per minute.

Muscle contraction The process which creates tension in the muscles, which creates movement

Lactic acid Waste product of anaerobic exercise; it causes fatigue.

Links to other units

You can find further information on this topic in Unit R044.

Thinking about the activity **improves the concentration and focus** of the performer. This focus on important cues means the performer begins to get into the right frame of mind, concentrating on the upcoming performance. Improved concentration means that reaction time is speeded up and decisions are made quicker, for example deciding whom to pass to and how to move to avoid being tackled. Improved focus makes it less likely that injury will occur. A performer who is more focused on producing the best gymnastics technique is less likely to stumble, fall and injure themselves and more likely to have a good performance.

Taking part in a warm up will **increase motivation**. Thinking about the task ahead will increase your drive to perform well – for example, if you know that a good performance in a match will enable the team to win or gain promotion at the end of the season – and you will try harder. A lack of motivation may lead to performers in contact sports becoming involved in a half-hearted manner. This can often lead to injury, for example through the use of poor tackling technique in rugby.

During a warm up, there is time for **mental rehearsal**. Mental rehearsal involves visualising or imagining each aspect of the activity before performing it. This increases confidence because you have a clear picture of what you intend to do during your performance and can avoid the distractions of the crowds or the opposition. For example, a rugby player may use mental rehearsal to mentally practise their goal-kicking technique. A trampolinist might use **imagery** to focus on their routine and not be distracted by the crowd. A hockey player might use visualisation to control their arousal and reduce their anxiety, and become less likely to attempt dangerous passes and tackles.

Another aspect of a warm up is the rehearsal of skills involved in the activity, which can be done either physically or mentally or, even better, both. Skill rehearsal will improve technique and, therefore, overall performance. Successfully practising a skill will improve confidence and speed up reaction time.

Key components of a warm up

Warm ups vary from person to person and from activity to activity, but there should be five key components of a warm up. Each component should be done in the following order:

1 **Pulse raising** – this should consist of exercises that slowly increase the heart rate and body temperature, for example a steady jog, running on the spot or skipping. If the activity involves another type of movement apart from running, then use that form of movement. For example, swimmers should raise their pulse through a slow swim, and cyclists should go for a short bike ride.

2 **Mobility** – these exercises take the joints through their full range of motion. For example, a golfer might perform arm swings and hip circles.

Key terms

Mental rehearsal
Visualising or imagining each aspect of the activity before performing it.

Imagery When a performer pictures something in their head to try to maintain focus.

Group activity

Using the list created in the getting started exercise, identify whether the activities have physical or psychological benefits.

Stretch activity

For each of the activities highlighted in the group activity above, describe how these benefits will help to prevent injuries.

Figure 1.21 Pulse raiser

17

3 **Dynamic movements** – these involve changes in speed and direction. For example, a basketball player could undertake short sprints with changes of speed and direction because these are the types of movement that may occur during a tournament. They might use cones or other players to dodge in between.

4 **Stretching** – this part of the warm up aims to lengthen the muscles in preparation for exercise. There are several different types of stretches that could be used:

- Static stretching is when a stretch is carried out and the position held for about 30 seconds.
- Passive stretching is a form of static stretching where an external force such as gravity or a partner forces the joint into a new position.
- **Dynamic stretches** involve stretching while you are moving.
- Ballistic stretching is a form of dynamic stretching but uses a bouncing motion.

There are also developmental stretches, where the stretch is increased every few seconds. Some stretches are linked to the particular sport, such as the 'open the gate' groin walk for football.

5 **Skill rehearsal phase** – this part of a warm up involves practising the actions that are about to be used in the game or activity. For example, footballers might practise the skill of dribbling around a series of cones; netball or basketball players might practise passing by going through some passing drills. If the warm up was in preparation for an exercise programme, the performer might wish to prepare the muscles and joints by practising the common movement patterns that might be used in the exercise session, such as lunges, press-ups or squats.

Physical benefits of a cool down

Sports performers should follow up a period of physical activity with additional cool down exercises.

A cool down helps the body **transition back to a resting state** by **gradually lowering**:

- heart rate
- blood pressure
- body temperature
- breathing rate.

This gradual slowing of bodily functions still circulates blood and oxygen to the muscles and stops the performer feeling dizzy and nauseous.

A cool down also helps to prevent blood pooling in the legs and **removes the waste products of exercise** (mainly lactic acid), **reducing the risk of muscle soreness which** sometimes occurs following training. When muscles are overstressed, it causes minor damage that allows tiny amounts of fluid to leak out from the

Key term

Dynamic stretching
A stretch that takes the body through the range of motion but is not held for any length of time.

Figure 1.22 'Open the gate' groin stretch

Group activity

In your group, consider the warm up you used in the getting started activity. List the key components that were used.

Stretch activity

Which components were missing or were not needed in the warm up you used in the getting started activity? Give reasons for your decisions.

Figure 1.23 Netball passing drills

muscles, resulting in swelling and soreness. The soreness usually appears 24–48 hours after the exercise. A cool down **aids recovery by stretching muscles**, which also decreases the risk of pulled muscle injuries. These together help performers to exercise again the following day and avoid delayed onset muscle soreness (DOMS).

Key components of a cool down

There are two key components of a cool down. First, the performer should take part in **pulse lowering** exercises, such as easy movements like walking and jogging, which **gradually** lower the heart rate and reduce body temperature. Then the performer should do some **stretching**, such as maintenance or static stretches. The purpose of a maintenance stretch is to return the muscles that have been used in the activity back to their normal length. These stretches should be held for approximately 10–15 seconds. For example, if a performer has been involved in activities where there is lots of running, hamstring stretches should form part of the cool down to help return the hamstrings to their normal length.

Specific needs which a warm up and cool down must consider

There are several specific needs that should be considered before deciding on the content of a warm up and cool down routine. These needs may be split into:

- the characteristics of the individual or group
- the suitability as preparation for a particular activity/sport
- environmental factors.

Characteristics of the individual or group

The organiser must take into consideration:

- the **age** of the participants, for example young children require a warm up of lower intensity and shorter duration than that needed for adults
- the **experience** of the participants; more experienced participants need a warm up involving a higher level of skill in the skill rehearsal phase compared to someone of lower ability
- individuals' strengths and weaknesses
- individual **fitness levels** of the participants and the various factors affecting a performer's fitness, such as recovery from a recent injury, illness, previous exercise routines, and levels of flexibility, strength and power
- individual levels of motivation
- an individual's state of health or any **medical conditions**; previous injuries such as muscle strains or a joint sprain, or health issues such as asthma, diabetes or epilepsy, will require the routine to be adapted
- specific disabilities or mental or physical health issues

Figure 1.24 Stretching as part of a cool down

Group activity

Each group should choose a different sport. Create a storyboard showing a range of cool down techniques/ activities that would be suitable for that sport.

Stretch activity

On the storyboard produced by your group, add details that explain the physical benefits of these cool down activities.

Read about it

Benefits of cooling down after exercise:

www.exercise4weightloss.com/ benefits-of-cooling-down.html

www.verywellfit.com/what-is- a-cool-down-3495457

- the **size of the group** involved; there should be enough space for the number of participants, otherwise injuries may occur through people bumping into each other.

Suitability as preparation for a particular activity/sport

A warm up should reflect the movements and activities that will be part of the sport. A warm up that takes place on the side of the swimming pool is probably not suitable for an activity that is going to be based in the pool itself. Similarly, a warm up for a skiing session that takes place indoors prior to putting on the skis is probably not suitable. Warm up and cool down routines need to be specific to the activity being undertaken.

Environmental factors

Several environmental factors can affect the content of a warm up and cool down.

The **weather** is an important environmental factor to consider, in particular the temperature. Although warming up in warm weather is quite pleasant, warming up in hot weather subjects participants to the possibility of heatstroke. In hot conditions, it might be better to warm up indoors or in shade. It is difficult to cool down if the weather is hot, and there will be a need to take on extra water during a cool down. In hot weather, the body's temperature may get so high during exercise that cold water sprays or ice baths are needed to return core temperature to normal.

It may be difficult to warm up in very cold weather, and again an indoor warm up may be beneficial, as might an indoor cool down. Windy conditions exaggerate the cold because of wind chill. Any muscles that have been strained during the activity tend to stay tight in a cold environment, so a longer cool down may be necessary.

The availability of **suitable facilities** for the warm up and cool down needs to be considered. There must be sufficient space to avoid overcrowding, and the surface available needs to be appropriate for the intended activities. If the facilities and/or surface are poor, the risk of injury is increased.

Know it!

1 Explain the physical benefits of a warm up and cool down.
2 Describe a range of warm up and cool down techniques and activities, and the areas of the body that they target.
3 What are the effects of a poor warm up or cool down, or of not warming up or cooling down at all?
4 Describe the psychological effects that a warm up can have on a performance.

Group activity

Within your group, suggest what environmental factors need to be considered when planning a cool down activity.

Stretch activity

In pairs, plan a cool down activity that considers the characteristics of the individual, the suitability of the cool down for a particular activity/sport and the environmental factors involved.

Classroom discussion

Discuss the physical and psychological benefits of completing a suitable warm up.

LO3 Know how to respond to injuries within a sporting context

Playing sport or being involved in any physical activity increases the risk of an injury occurring. All those involved should know how to respond to injuries within a sporting context.

Acute and chronic injuries

Injuries in sport are usually divided into two types:

- **Acute injuries** are those that happen quickly and are caused by sudden trauma, such as impacts or collisions. Examples include a hard tackle in rugby or football, or being hit by the ball in cricket or hockey. Acute injuries cause immediate pain and usually produce some swelling and loss of function, for example having pain in an ankle and being unable to walk on it properly. Common acute sporting injuries include sprained ankles and hamstring tears.
- **Chronic injuries** are those that are caused by continuous or repeated stress on an area of the body such as a bone, muscle, ligaments or tendons. They are often called **overuse injuries**, as they develop gradually over a period of time. Examples include **shin splints**, **tennis elbow** and Achilles **tendonitis**.

Types, causes and treatment of common sports injuries

Many different injuries can occur during physical activity, but it is possible to group some of them together according to their types, causes and treatment.

Soft tissue injuries

Soft tissue injuries happen when trauma or overuse occurs to muscles, tendons or ligaments. They can be either acute or chronic. The most common soft tissue injuries are the result of a sudden unexpected or uncontrolled movement, such as slipping awkwardly in muddy conditions and rolling your ankle over. These sudden twisting and stretching forces stretch or tear the fibres of muscles, tendons or ligaments. They may even cause the muscle, tendon or ligament to detach from its anchor point on a bone. Tears to muscle fibres are usually called **strains**, while tears to ligaments are called **sprains**.

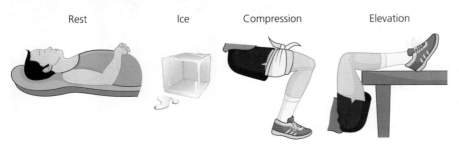

Rest   Ice   Compression   Elevation

Figure 1.25 RICE

Overuse injuries

Many common sporting injuries are overuse injuries. Overuse injuries are also called chronic injuries. They are subtle and usually occur over time, making them difficult to recognise. They are caused by repetitive minor damage to the tendons, bones and joints, often as a result of excessive activity or lack of rest. Common examples include tendonitis, tennis or golfer's elbow, and shin splints.

Overuse injuries are best treated using the **RICE** method. Stretching, massage and bandaging will also help. More serious cases may involve visits to a physiotherapist and the application of heat packs.

Tendonitis is a common overuse injury. The symptoms include pain in the affected tendon and restricted movements because of the pain. There is often accompanying inflammation and swelling. One common type of tendonitis is tennis elbow, usually caused by the repetitive swinging of the arm when hitting tennis balls. **Golfer's elbow** is a similar injury caused by the repetitive swinging of golf clubs when hitting golf balls.

Tendonitis injuries are treated with rest and ice packs. Bandaging and mobility exercises often help. Anti-inflammatory medicines and ultrasound may need to be used in serious cases.

Fractures

A **fracture** is a partial or complete break in a bone. It is an acute injury. There are two main types of fracture: closed and open.

A **closed fracture** is one where there is relatively little damage to the surrounding tissues because the bone has hardly moved. An **open fracture** is one where there is considerable damage to the tissues because the fractured bone has broken through the skin. Open fractures have a high risk of infection.

Fractures are usually caused by sudden trauma, such as an awkward fall or bad landing, or impact with another player in a tackle or collision. Fractures are more common in contact sports.

Fractures require treatment at a hospital, where an X-ray can identify the problem and the corresponding treatment. Most limb fractures are treated with plaster casts, splints and possibly slings.

Read about it

What is a fracture?
www.medicalnewstoday.com/articles/173312.php
Fractures:
https://orthoinfo.aaos.org/en/diseases--conditions/fractures-broken-bones

Read about it

Soft tissue injuries:
http://thephysiotherapyclinics.com/soft-tissue-injuries

http://sma.org.au/resources-advice/injury-fact-sheets/soft-tissue-injuries

🔑 Key terms

RICE Acronym for rest, ice, compression and elevation – the treatment for soft tissue injuries.

Golfer's elbow Tendon injury due to repetitive actions such as golf strokes.

Fracture Partial or complete break in a bone.

Closed fracture Broken bone with no break in the skin.

Open fracture Broken bone in which the skin is also broken, exposing the bone.

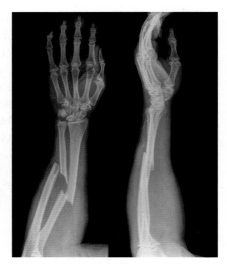

Figure 1.26 X-ray of fractured forearm

Concussion

Concussion is caused by impacts to the head, either from a collision or from contact with the ground or a piece of equipment. It is an acute injury in which the brain is shaken inside the skull. This often causes a loss of consciousness, which may only last a few seconds. Other symptoms include dizziness, nausea or **vomiting**, loss of memory, loss of balance and headaches.

Concussion, even suspected concussion, requires medical assistance and possibly hospital treatment. Temporary relief may be gained by applying a cold compress. If a player has concussion then there is a significant health risk from another blow to the head. In this case players may have to miss several matches (e.g. in rugby).

Abrasions

An **abrasion** is an acute injury involving surface damage to the skin that results in grazes (where skin has been scraped away) and cuts. Abrasions are often caused by falling or tripping onto hard or rough ground. They may also be caused by being hit by a piece of equipment, or by skin rubbing against equipment, clothing or the ground, especially artificial surfaces. Abrasions often result from being kicked, punched or tackled.

Abrasions may be treated by cleaning or sterilising the damaged area and covering them with plasters or bandages.

Contusions

Contusion is another name for a bruise. Contusions are very common in physical activity and often result from colliding with another player or piece of equipment, or falling, tackling or tripping.

Many contusions go untreated but sometimes RICE treatment may help.

Blisters

Blisters are a defence mechanism that help to repair skin damage caused by friction. They are small bags of fluid that develop under the skin to protect the underlying tissue. Blisters form when skin rubs against poorly fitting footwear, or through wearing badly fitting socks or no socks at all. Blisters can also form when you have to grip a piece of equipment tightly, for example a tennis racket. Blisters are more likely to form in hot weather because sweating makes it easier for the feet to move around inside socks and trainers.

Blisters should be cleaned and sterilised if needed, and left to heal naturally. They may be covered with a plaster or dressing.

Cramp

Cramp is an involuntary painful contraction of muscles caused by a lack of water and/or salt to the muscles. It is often caused by

Key terms

Concussion Injury in which the brain is shaken inside the skull.

Vomiting Being sick/throwing up.

Abrasion Surface damage to the skin – grazes and cuts.

Contusion Bruise.

Blisters Bubbles of fluid under the skin caused by friction.

Cramp Involuntary contraction of muscle.

Read about it

Concussion:

www.nhs.uk/conditions/Concussion

Figure 1.27 Stretching off cramp

excessive exercise, or overuse or overstretching of the muscles. Cramp may also result from poor hydration.

It may be lessened by stretching and/or massaging the affected muscle.

Injuries related to children

Sever's disease presents as pain in the heel of young children because of an inflammation of the growth plate of the heel. It is caused by repetitive stress and is therefore particularly common in physically active children.

Sever's disease often cures itself through rest or as the child grows. Extra treatment may consist of elevation of the heel, regular stretching of the hamstring and calf muscles, and using RICE.

Osgood-Schlatter's disease is a pain in the knee that occurs in children as a result of growth spurts, where the bones in the knee joint grow too quickly for the surrounding tendons. It may also be caused by repeated stress or overuse. The best treatment is RICE, but recurring Osgood-Schlatter's disease needs medical advice.

How to respond to injuries and medical conditions in a sporting context

The range of different sports and physical activities that exist means that the variety of possible sporting injuries that may be encountered is huge. Some can be serious, possibly life-threatening, and require hospitalisation, while others are relatively minor and may be treated with simple home care. How to respond to injuries and medical conditions in a sporting context depends on the severity of the injury and the knowledge of those in the immediate vicinity of the injury.

SALTAPS on-field assessment routine

SALTAPS involves an assessment of whether an injured performer should be allowed to continue to play or train. The acronym stands for see, ask, look, touch, active, passive and strength. The most qualified and experienced individual in the vicinity should use the following guidelines to assess the injury:

- **S**ee – ask if anyone saw what happened; stop the activity; check the injured person's facial expressions, their posture and behaviour.
- **A**sk – ask the injured player what happened and how they feel; ask them where it hurts and ask questions about the injury, such as what type of pain is involved.
- **L**ook – look for signs of injury such as bleeding, bruising, swelling or deformity; if appropriate, compare the injured limb to the opposite limb – do they look similar or different?
- **T**ouch – examine the injured site for pain and tenderness; can you feel any abnormalities?

Key terms

Sever's disease Heel pain caused by an inflamed growth plate.

Osgood-Schlatter's disease Knee pain caused by growth spurts.

SALTAPS Acronym for see, ask, look, touch, active, passive and strength – an on-field assessment routine performers.

Group activity

In pairs, research injuries that three top performing sports people from three different sports have suffered, for example one footballer, one skier and one boxer. Create a table that lists the injury type, the cause and the treatment.

- **A**ctive – can the performer move the limb themselves? Does it hurt to move? Can they manage any non-weight-bearing movement?
- **P**assive – move the limb/joint through the full range of movement, noting the injured person's reaction to the movement.
- **S**trength – can the performer support their own weight? Are they able to get up following the injury? Can they play on?

If the injury is serious, the SALTAPS process needs to be stopped at the appropriate stage.

Read about it

Prezi presentation on SALTAPS:

https://prezi.com/p8dbuqjzfhqp/ sport-injuries-saltaps

RICE

For acute but less serious injuries to soft tissues, the initial treatment is often the RICE procedure. Soft tissue injuries often involve inflammation, and the purpose of RICE is to reduce swelling, ease pain and prevent further damage:

- **R**est – the performer should stop the activity to prevent further injury; they should avoid using the injured part and try to keep their weight off it, possibly with the help of crutches.
- **I**ce – an ice pack should be applied to the affected area for 10–30 minutes; if no ice is available, a bag of frozen food such as peas works just as well; the ice reduces swelling and pain.
- **C**ompression – bandage the injured part to reduce swelling and help support the injured area.
- **E**levation – keep the injured leg, knee, arm, elbow or wrist raised above the level of the heart; this reduces blood flow to the injured area, again helping to reduce swelling.

RICE should only be used for acute soft tissue injuries. It is not suitable for injuries where there is heavy blood loss as it might increase the risk of infection. It should also not be used where its application may cause pain or where the injured person should be taken directly to hospital or requires a 999 call.

Figure 1.28 Use of ice to reduce swelling

Stretching and massage

Stretching and massage involves manipulating soft tissues. It:

- increases the flow of blood to the affected body part and increases flexibility
- helps to relax muscles and relieve tension
- helps to manage pain and delayed onset muscle soreness (DOMS).

Taping, bandaging, splints, slings

Taping and strapping are often used to support weak or injured muscles and joints and, in doing so, reduce pain.

Bandaging helps to prevent swelling or decrease blood flow to the area. Bandaging can reduce pain and gives support. It can also keep the area immobilised so that you cannot move it. Bandaging is also used to stop bleeding and help prevent infection.

Figure 1.29 Bandaging

A **splint** is commonly used for limb injuries such as acute fractures or sprains. The purpose of a splint is to immobilise and protect the injured limb, to allow time for rest and healing to occur, and to lessen pain.

A **sling** supports joints and helps to hold the injured part in place and in the correct position. Slings reduce the stress around the injured part and help to prevent further injury through impact. They may also elevate the injured part, which helps to reduce swelling and to relieve pain.

Key terms

Splint Plastic or fibreglass support for limb fractures and sprains.

Sling Support, usually of folded cloth, to immobilise and rest the injured limb.

Ice therapy Use of ice to reduce pain and swelling.

Heat treatment Use of heat to reduce pain and stiffness, and to speed up healing.

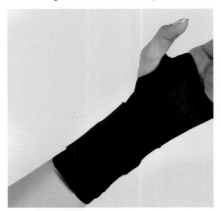

Figure 1.30 Arm splint

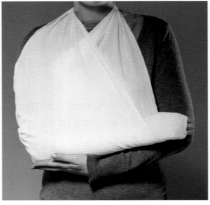

Figure 1.31 Arm sling

Hot and cold treatments

Hot and cold treatments are an effective way to manage sports injuries.

Ice therapy is the application of an ice pack to the affected area for 15–20 minutes every two to three hours. A bag of frozen peas, or similar, will work well. The ice pack should be wrapped in a towel so that it does not directly touch the skin and cause an ice burn. Ice therapy is commonly used for contusions, and it is also good treatment for sprained ankles and as pain relief. Instant ice packs and cold sprays are also available for the treatment of sprains, strains and bruises.

Heat treatment is used for many sports-related musculo-skeletal injuries. There are many forms of heat treatment, with the most effective often depending on the injury in question. Timescale is also an important factor when deciding whether to use heat treatment. The benefit of heat treatment is that heat:

- reduces pain
- reduces stiffness
- decreases muscle spasm
- increases blood flow to the area, which promotes healing.

Heat treatment can be as simple as running hot water over the injured part. Heat lamps are also available, as are heat packs and reusable gel packs that can be warmed up in the microwave to provide relief.

Table 1.1 Ice therapy versus heat treatment

	Ice therapy	Heat treatment
What it does	Reduces blood flow Reduces swelling and inflammation Controls pain	Increases blood flow Reduces stiffness Relieves pain
When to use it	Immediately First 24–72 hours of the injury	When swelling has gone down 72 hours after the injury occurred
How to apply it	Ice pack, ice block or bag of frozen peas (wrapped in a towel – do not apply directly to the skin) Apply for no longer than 20-minute intervals	Heat bag, hot water bottle or electric heat pack (wrapped in a cloth) Apply for no longer than 20-minute intervals
Best for	Sprains, strains, slips, falls, migraines Also useful for overuse injuries and chronic pain in athletes	Loosening up tight muscles and joints Pain relief for chronic pain and tension headaches

Stretch activity

Go back to the getting started activity and add in any further injuries you can think of. Include details about the probable causes of these injuries and how they might be prevented.

Read about it

Treating pain with heat and cold:
https://www.healthline.com/health/chronic-pain/treating-pain-with-heat-and-cold

Action plan to respond to injuries and medical conditions in a sporting context

It is important that the organisers of a physical activity have an action plan of how to respond to injuries and medical conditions that might arise. This is important so that people participating in an activity know that they are going to be safe.

The action plan is also there so that the people in charge know what to do in the event of an emergency. It should be planned and practised in advance.

Having an action plan reduces the risk of minor injuries becoming more serious injuries when someone takes part in sport. Minor issues can be addressed before they develop into something major, as both the employees of a sports organisation and the people doing or watching the sport immediately know what to do in the event of a problem occurring.

Emergency action plans in a sporting context

All sports clubs have a responsibility and a duty of care to ensure that a safe environment is available to those present at an event, spectators as well as athletes. This includes having a clearly documented **emergency action plan (EAP)** that outlines the actions and procedures that need to be fulfilled in the event of an emergency.

Key term

Emergency action plan (EAP) Written document identifying what action to take in the event of an emergency at a sporting event.

An EAP has three main components:

1 **Emergency personnel**
2 **Emergency communication** – knowledge of how to contact emergency services, such as the location of the nearest telephone and emergency contact numbers.
3 **Emergency equipment** – details of where first-aid kits and other relevant materials may be found for use in an emergency.

Having a simple, organised and safe approach to an emergency incident could make a big difference to its outcome. Once an EAP has been created it must be communicated to coaches, first aiders and any other volunteers taking on the responsibility of first-aid and incident management. This is best done by having the EAP printed and on display at the event and made available to all visitors.

Stretch activity

The headteacher of the local high school requires an EAP to be created before agreeing to host a large sporting event. Create the initial outline of the EAP.

Read about it

Emergency action plans:
www.nays.org/resources/more/emergency-action-plans

www.nata.org/sites/default/files/white-paper-emergency-action-plan.pdf

How to create an emergency action plan:

www.reactfirst.co.uk/live/tips34.asp

Emergency Action Plan

If an athlete has a life-threatening emergency, one person should stay with them and call 999.

Information for the dispatcher:
Indicate your need for an ambulance

Current location's address: _____

Your call back number: _____

Injured person's approximate age and medical issue (e.g. head injury, spine injury, heart condition)

Directions for first responders to find the entrance to the facility and find the injured person.

A second person should be waiting at the entrance to help first responders locate the injured person.
This person should also call the injured athlete's emergency contact number (if they are not already present).

A third person should serve as a 'runner' to retrieve medical and first-aid supplies as needed for the person that is attending to the injured athlete.

A fourth person should take responsibility for any other people present in the facility and ensure that the area around the injured person is clear.

Address of nearest hospital: _____

Phone number of hospital: _____

Figure 1.32 A typical emergency action plan

Although the initial creation of an EAP may be intensive, it could save someone's life.

Emergency personnel

The EAP must detail who the key on-site **emergency personnel** are and who is responsible in the event of an emergency. People need to know who the first responder is, who the qualified first aiders are and who the coach is. If there is an emergency, everybody should know whom they need to contact immediately and, if these people are not present, where or how to contact them.

Emergency communication

The EAP must contain details of **emergency communication**; with relevant contact numbers for the emergency services (999), the location of the nearest telephone and any specialist provision on-site.

Emergency equipment

The EAP must contain details of the location of all **emergency equipment** at the facility. This could include where first-aid kits, stretchers, defibrillators and evacuation chairs are located, for example, in case they are needed in an emergency.

 Key terms

Emergency personnel
People who are responsible in an emergency, such as first responders and qualified first aiders.

Emergency communication
Details of whom to contact in an emergency.

Emergency equipment
Equipment required in an emergency situation, for example first-aid kits, stretchers and defibrillators.

Know it!

1 Define acute and chronic injuries.
2 Describe how the following sports injuries may be caused and prevented.
    a Ankle sprain
    b Fractured finger
    c Concussion
3 Describe how the following common sports injuries can be treated.
    a Muscle strain
    b Blisters
    c Tennis elbow
    d Cramp

L04 Know how to respond to common medical conditions

There are several common medical conditions that may affect sports performance. All those involved in organising sport should know how to respond to them.

Symptoms of common medical conditions

The symptoms of common medical conditions should be known to all those involved in sport.

Asthma

Asthma is a common, long-term lung condition that causes occasional breathing difficulties. It affects people of all ages and often starts in childhood, although it can develop for the first time in adults. The most common symptoms of asthma are coughing (especially during exercise), shortness of breath, a feeling of tightness in the chest and wheezing, which is a whistling or squeaky sound in your chest when you breathe, especially when exhaling.

There is no cure for asthma currently but there are simple treatments that can help keep the symptoms under control, so that it does not have a big impact on a performer's life.

Diabetes

Diabetes is a serious condition that causes the body's blood sugar level to be too high. When we eat, some of the food is converted into glucose (sugar), which finds its way into our blood and gives us energy. Normally we release a hormone called insulin to control the levels of glucose that are being used for energy. If you have diabetes, however, this system does not work. There are two main types of diabetes:

- **Type 1** – people with type 1 diabetes are unable to make any insulin to lower blood sugar levels and have to rely on insulin injections. It is referred to as **insulin-dependent diabetes**.
- **Type 2** – people with type 2 diabetes either cannot produce enough insulin or their insulin does not work effectively. It is referred to as **insulin-resistant diabetes**. This type of diabetes is regulated through careful dietary control, although some people may need to take insulin if diet alone cannot help.

In both types of diabetes, glucose builds up in the blood (hyperglycaemia) and causes problems. People with hyperglycaemia need to urinate frequently, get very thirsty and feel very tired. They may also lose weight, are prone to infections, and cuts and wounds take longer to heal. In the long term, high glucose levels in the blood can damage the heart, kidneys, eyes and feet.

If a diabetic person injects too much insulin, or exercises excessively, they may develop low blood sugar (hypoglycaemia).

Getting started

Asthma, diabetes and epilepsy are common medical conditions. Create a mind map showing what you know about these conditions.

Key terms

Asthma Lung condition that causes occasional breathing difficulties.

Diabetes Condition in which blood sugar levels are unregulated by the body.

Insulin-dependent diabetes Type 1 diabetes; requires insulin injections.

Insulin-resistant diabetes Type 2 diabetes; usually managed through careful dietary control.

Symptoms can include shakiness, dizziness, sweating, hunger and irritability. If untreated, it can lead to drowsiness, slurred speech, confusion and unconsciousness.

Epilepsy

Epilepsy is a condition of the nervous system in which brain activity becomes abnormal, causing seizures or periods of unusual behaviour and sensations, and sometimes loss of awareness. Anyone can develop epilepsy: it affects both men and women of all ethnic backgrounds and ages.

Seizure symptoms can vary widely. Some people with epilepsy simply stare blankly for a few seconds during a seizure, while others repeatedly shake their arms or legs. Other seizure symptoms include falling unconscious, losing control of your bowel or bladder, falling down suddenly or muscles becoming stiff.

How to respond to common medical conditions

It is important to be aware that asthma attacks, diabetes and epileptic seizures can occur without much prior warning, and to know how to respond to these common medical conditions.

Ensure awareness of participant's medical conditions prior to commencing physical activity

It is important that individuals who suffer from these conditions are fully aware of the possibility that an attack, episode or seizure can occur. They must ensure that the organisers of a sports event are aware of any pre-existing medical conditions before commencing physical activity, so that appropriate action can be taken immediately.

Responding to an asthma attack

People with asthma are usually aware of when an asthma attack occurs. Treatment is therefore mainly to provide reassurance and keep calm. The person will probably have a suitable inhaler, and you may need to help them locate it. In very rare cases, access to the emergency services may be required. Participants should ensure that event organisers are aware that they have an inhaler available and where it is located.

Responding to a diabetic episode

The different types of diabetes require different treatments. A person with type 1 diabetes (insulin-dependent) will know that they have it. They need to check their blood sugar levels regularly. If their blood sugar is too high (hyperglycaemic), they should inject themselves with insulin; if their blood sugar is too low (hypoglycaemic), they should have, or be given, simple sweet foods or liquids, such as sweets or fruit juice.

A person with type 2 diabetes (insulin-resistant) needs to control their blood sugar levels through their diet and may have medicines to help lower blood sugar levels, which you may need to help them to find.

Key term

Epilepsy Condition causing abnormal brain activity leading to seizures.

Group activity

Go back to your getting started activity and add any new information that you have discovered about these common medical conditions – use a different coloured pen.

Responding to an epileptic seizure

An epileptic seizure can vary from a momentary loss of awareness to a loss of consciousness and convulsions.

A person suffering from a partial (or focal) seizure may become unaware of their surroundings or what they are doing. They should be guided away from danger and kept calm. You should call the emergency services if this is their first seizure or if the seizure lasts for more than five minutes.

Tonic-clonic seizures are when the person goes stiff, loses consciousness, falls to the floor and begins to convulse or jerk. They should be protected from injury by removing nearby harmful objects and their head should be cushioned. The duration of the convulsions should be noted. Help their breathing by placing them in the **recovery position** once they have stopped jerking. Stay with them until they are fully recovered, be calm and reassuring. Call the emergency services if this is their first seizure, if the jerking lasts for more than five minutes, or they have a second tonic-clonic seizure without gaining consciousness.

1 Open the casualty's airway by gently tilting their head back and lifting their chin.

2 Straighten the casualty's limbs

3 Put the casualty's arm nearest to you out at right angles to their body, with the elbow bent and the palm facing up.

4 Take hold of the casualty's other hand and put the back of it against their opposite cheek – hold it there.

5 With your other hand, take hold of the casualty's far leg, just above the knee, and pull it up until the foot is flat on the floor.

6 Keeping their hand pressed against their cheek, gently roll the casualty towards you onto their side, using the knee as leverage.

Figure 1.33 The recovery position helps to keep the airway clear and prevent choking

When to refer the performer to a professional and how to do so

If an injury sustained cannot be treated by the most qualified person present, the performer should be referred to a medical professional. This could be when:

- the performer loses consciousness or has an obvious concussion
- the performer has potential or suspected fractures
- the performer has a recurring injury
- the injury is severe or the performer is in considerable pain
- the performer is struggling to breathe
- the coach or person in charge is unqualified to deal with the injury.

 Group activity

You have been asked to create an EPA for a sporting event to be held in the summer. You have been informed one of the performers has asthma. What plans do you need to have in place to ensure their safety?

Performers with known conditions should be referred to a medical professional if:

- they continue to show severe signs of asthma
- a type 1 diabetic does not have access to their insulin or they lapse into a diabetic coma
- they suffer an epileptic fit for the first time, or the fit lasts longer than five minutes or is repeated.

Contact professional help by dialling 999 and asking for an ambulance or, if it is easier or quicker, take the performer directly to the nearest accident and emergency (A&E) department. Less serious cases could be managed via referral to a first responder or a local NHS walk-in centre, or by asking the performer to contact their doctor or physiotherapist.

Classroom discussion

Discuss possible scenarios in which it would be appropriate to refer performers to a medical professional.

Know it!

1 Describe the symptoms and treatment of:
  a Asthma
  b Diabetes
  c Epilepsy
2 For each of the following conditions, suggest the symptoms that would require referring the patient to a medical professional:
  a Asthma
  b Diabetes
  c Epilepsy

Read about it

Asthma:
www.nhs.uk/conditions/asthma
Diabetes:
www.nhs.uk/conditions/diabetes
Epilepsy:
www.nhs.uk/conditions/epilepsy

Assessment preparation

1 Explain how extrinsic factors can influence the risk of injury to sports performers.   [8]
2 Poor posture can be caused by sporting, medical and lifestyle factors. Explain the causes of poor posture and how they may affect sports performance.   [8]
3 Explain the benefits of a warm up before starting physical activity.   [8]
4 Describe the key components of a cool down and explain the physical benefits that a cool down provides for a sports performer.   [8]

5 Explain the specific needs that should be considered by a sports coach when planning a warm up or cool down. [8]

6 Using practical examples, describe the causes, symptoms and treatment of different overuse injuries. [8]

7 Explain how, in a sporting context, SALTAPS can help a coach to respond to an injury. [8]

8 Explain the areas that make up an emergency action plan (EAP) in a sporting context. Detail the reasons for and the benefits of having an action plan in place. [8]

9 What are the symptoms and treatments for:
   a asthma   b diabetes   c epilepsy [6]

Mark scheme

To gain the top marks, you will need to:

● ensure your answers are well structured

● include appropriate terminology and technical terms

● carefully check for spelling, grammar and punctuation.

Specific guidance for each question is given in the table below.

1	Include a variety of extrinsic factors (at least four), making a wide range of points across the content mentioned in the specification. Include an evaluation.
2	Consider a wide range of points that have been covered in the specification. Demonstrate a good understanding through a detailed discussion of the causes of poor posture and how it may affect sports performance. Include an evaluation.
3	Consider a wide range of points that have been covered in the specification. Demonstrate a detailed understanding of the physical and psychological benefits of warming up. Include clear explanations.
4	Consider a wide range of points that have been covered in the specification and develop several of these, leading to an evaluation. Demonstrate a good understanding of the physical benefits through a detailed discussion.
5	Consider a wide range of points that have been covered in the specification and develop many of them to a high level. Demonstrate a detailed knowledge and understanding of the needs.
6	Demonstrate a detailed knowledge of overuse injuries. Make many valid points, most of them including causes, symptoms and treatments. Include examples from a range of different sports.
7	Consider many points that have been covered in the specification and develop several of them to a high level, leading to a clear evaluation. Demonstrate a good understanding through a detailed discussion.
8	Ensure that emergency personnel, emergency communication and emergency equipment are all covered. Demonstrate a good understanding through a detailed discussion. Consider many points that have been covered in the specification and develop several, leading to a clear evaluation.
9	Include one symptom and one treatment for each.

R042 Applying principles of training

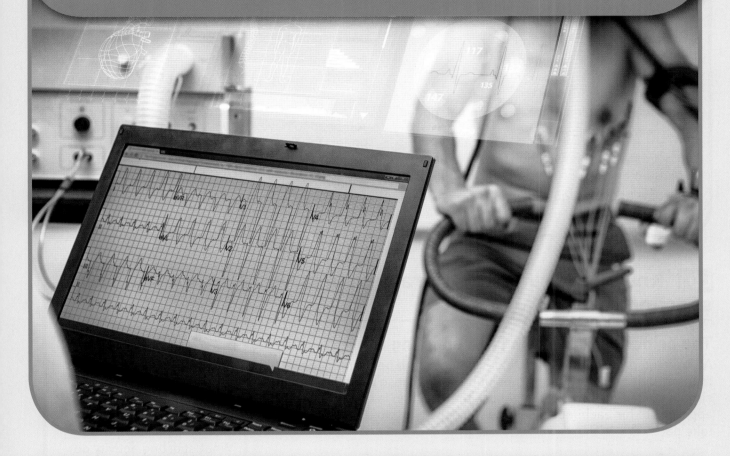

About this unit

By completing this unit, you will appreciate how coaches strive to keep their performers in peak condition and why this is important. The content covered includes how varying fitness tests are conducted and how the data gained from these tests can be used in the design of suitable and appropriate training programmes. In learning about training programmes, you will appreciate the importance of the principles of training and how these principles can be applied to suit the individual needs and sports being performed. You will understand how training can be designed and implemented to allow performers to reach their performance targets.

Learning outcomes

LO1 Know the principles of training in a sporting context

LO2 Know how training methods target different fitness components

LO3 Be able to conduct fitness tests

LO4 Be able to develop fitness training programmes

How will I be assessed?

You will be assessed over 30 guided learning hours. Approximately ten hours of internal assessment will be worth 60 marks (60 UMS). This unit is centre assessed and OCR moderated.

For LO1

You need to have knowledge and understanding of:
- the principles of training
- how the principles of training can be applied.

For LO2

You need to have knowledge and understanding of:
- aerobic and anaerobic exercise
- the components of fitness

- specific training methods for each of the fitness components.

For LO3

You need to have knowledge and understanding of:
- tests that assess fitness
- how to interpret the results of fitness tests.

For LO4

You need to have knowledge and understanding of:
- how to design a fitness training programme
- how to evaluate the effectiveness of the training programme.

LO1 Know the principles of training in a sporting context

The principles of training in a sporting context

All training programmes should be designed and performed in a manner that meets the principles of training. These principles are simple guidelines to follow to ensure that training is effective and appropriate for each individual and the activity in which they take part.

Progression (progressive overload)

When a person **overloads** their body, they are simply working harder than normal. Overloading results in the body adapting, so training eventually becomes easier. To continue the adaptation, training must show progression, that is, it must get harder. **Progressive overload** means gradually making training harder as it becomes too easy. To apply progressive overload, the 'principles of overload' must be applied. These can be remembered by using the acronym **FITTA**:

- **F**requency – how often the person trains
- **I**ntensity – how hard/intense the training is
- **T**ime – how long the session training should last
- **T**ype – the type of training being used
- **A**dherence – how strictly you stick to the training plan.

Getting started

In small groups, find out what sporting activities each person takes part in. Discuss how each person trains for their activity, noting down any similarities or differences in each person's training. Initially, this can be as simple as: 'What sporting activity do you take part in and what does training involve when preparing for that sport?'

Key terms

Overload Working harder than normal.

Progressive overload Gradually making training harder as it becomes too easy.

FITTA Principles of overload: frequency, intensity, time, type, adherence.

You must be able to apply these principles to different activity types. Progressive overload simply involves thinking about each of the FITTA principles and altering what is being done to ensure progression. Examples are given in Table 2.1.

Group activity

Try to come up with examples from different sporting activities of how progressive overload can be applied when training.

Table 2.1 Examples of applying the concept of progressive overload

Example	Current training programme	Changes that apply the concept of progressive overload
A rugby player who aims to increase their strength by using weights	Frequency: twice a week Intensity: lifting 75% of one rep maximum Time: each session lasts for 45 minutes Type: weight training Adherence: attending twice a week on most weeks	Frequency: train three times a week Intensity: increase intensity to 80% of one rep maximum Time: increase session time to one hour Type: continue weight training but include some free weights and resistance machines Adherence: stick rigidly to attending three times a week
A sprinter who uses interval training when working on their speed	Frequency: twice a week Intensity: they perform eight sets of sprints at 80% of maximal effort, with a two-minute rest between each set Time: each session lasts 30 minutes Type: interval training Adherence: training twice a week on most weeks	Frequency: train three times a week Intensity: increase to ten sets at 85% of maximal effort; reduce recovery time to one minute 45 seconds Time: increase session time to 45 minutes Type: continue interval training but incorporate some weight training to work on strength Adherence: stick rigidly to attending three times a week

Specificity

As a training principle, **specificity** simply means that training should be suited to the sporting activity being trained for. Therefore, training should focus on:

- movements and skills that are used in the activity
- the muscles that are used in the activity.

Key term

Specificity Making training suited to the movements, skills and muscles that are used in an activity.

Figure 2.1 Swimmers tend to make their training specific to their sport by using the swimming action when training; this could involve continuous swimming or possibly interval training

Figure 2.2 Football players incorporate skills such as passing, shooting and dribbling into their training, as these are specific to their sport

Figure 2.3 Netball players work the muscles in their arms and legs to allow them to pass with force and change direction at speed; this could involve some weight training, circuits and agility work

Figure 2.4 Rowers are likely to lift weights using the muscles in their torso, arms and legs, as these muscles help to pull the oars through the water; this allows them to develop the muscles that they need to use in their event

Reversibility/regression

Reversibility/regression as a training principle simply refers to the concept of 'use it or lose it'. In other words, if you stop training your fitness level will regress (you will lose your fitness). Whatever training adaptations you have gained will be lost if you stop training, for example if you are faster you will start to become slower, if you are stronger you will start to lose some strength. There are a number of reasons why a performer may decide to (or need to) stop training, such as:

- an injury that prevents them from training
- they have other commitments which they deem more important
- they lack the motivation to continue training.

The simple way to prevent reversibility/regression from happening is to adhere to the set training plan. However, sometimes reversibility is beyond a performer's control. An anterior cruciate ligament (ACL) tear in the knee tends to need surgery and will usually mean the performer is not back in full training for approximately six months. Their fitness levels will regress considerably during this time.

Moderation

Moderation refers to taking individual characteristics and circumstances into consideration when designing a training programme. Factors that should be considered include:

- **Age** – younger people need a different amount of training to older people. Equally, elderly people may not be able to train as much as those younger than them. Very young performers should avoid heavy weight training, as it can stunt the growth of their bones.
- **Gender** – there are natural physiological differences between an average male and an average female performer, for example men have a higher VO_2 max on average than women (this is the maximum volume of oxygen that can be consumed in one minute).

🔑 Key terms

Reversibility/regression 'Use it or lose it' – if you stop training, you will lose fitness.

Moderation Taking individual characteristics and circumstances into consideration when designing a training programme.

- **Environment** – when designing a training session, the environment in which that training is to take place will be a major factor. For example, what equipment is available? How safe is the surface? What footwear should be worn? What is the weather forecast if outdoors?

- **Experience** – the experience level of those taking part will affect how training should be designed. A group of experienced athletes may be able to simply get on with their session with little to no supervision. A group of novices will need more guidance. Similarly, if the session includes both young athletes and mature performers, the coach will need to think about how to divide the group; for example, do they pair young athletes with mature athletes so that the mature athletes can assist the younger ones? Do they split up the mature athletes to receive more specialist training, while the young athletes receive relatively basic guidance? Is an induction programme appropriate?

Variance

The term **variance** comes from the word 'variety'. As a training principle, this involves performers altering and changing elements of their training in order to prevent boredom. Figure 2.5 gives some examples of how the principle of variance could be applied to training.

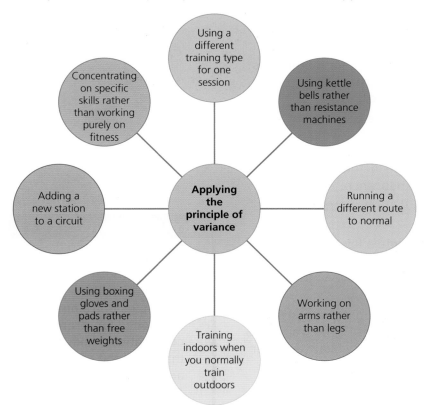

Figure 2.5 Applying the principle of variance

 Key term

Variance Altering and changing elements of training in order to prevent boredom.

 Group activity

Design a poster to be displayed in a local leisure centre. The poster should act as a guide for those training at the leisure centre on how to follow the principles of training. Make sure that progressive overload, specificity, reversibility/ regression, moderation and variance are included in the guidance given.

 Classroom discussion

With reference to performers who play team sports such as football, rugby, hockey or netball, discuss how the principles of training can be applied within training sessions. Include some detail about how variance could be incorporated into sessions and how moderation may be needed when there are different age groups involved.

In doing something slightly different to normal, the body is given a different challenge and, mentally, this can motivate performers to try out the new task or activity. Equally, if a performer works on skills rather than purely on fitness, they are being better prepared for the sporting activity.

Example of how to apply the principles of training

In this example, we will consider an athlete who is training to compete in a marathon.

- **Specificity** – the training needs to be specific to marathon running, therefore the athlete will inevitably use the running technique when carrying out continuous training. It will be more appropriate to complete training runs on the road rather than the treadmill. They may lift relatively light weights using the main muscles in the legs, which help them to run.
- **Progressive overload** – the athlete will apply the principles of overload:
  - ○ Frequency – as training gets easier they will increase the number of sessions per week, for example from two to three sessions.
  - ○ Intensity – they will use their heart rate as a guide to intensity of training. If they are performing at 65 per cent of their maximum heart rate (220 minus their age), they may well progress to working at 70 per cent of their maximum heart rate.
  - ○ Time – if the athlete begins training by running for 30 minutes continuously, they will need to gradually increase their continuous running time to 2 hours or more.
  - ○ Type – the athlete is likely to use continuous running but should run some different sessions through the week – normally a mix of short sprints, long slow runs, and medium length medium pace runs. They may also include some light weight training to work on muscular endurance.
  - ○ Adherence – the athlete adheres strictly to their training schedule to prevent regression.
- **Reversibility/regression** Allowing an athlete a few weeks off in the middle of a training programme will reverse their previous progress. An injured athlete may need weeks or even months off, so avoiding injuries is critical.
- **Moderation** While the training steadily builds up, the athlete still needs rest days, particularly after hard sessions. If the training is continuously too hard for the athlete they are very likely to suffer an injury.
- **Variance** – the athlete may wish to add some low-intensity weight training and to follow different running routes to prevent boredom. They may also decide to do a different activity occasionally, for example swimming, to provide some variety to their aerobic training.

Stretch activity

1 Describe all of the principles of training.

2 Explain how the principles of training can be applied for a range of activities. Make sure that all of the principles are covered for all of the activities. If you find a principle hard to explain for one activity, choose a different activity.

Know it!

1 List the principles of training.
2 Explain what each principle of training means.
3 Apply each principle of training to a range of different sporting activities.
4 Explain how the application of the principles of training would vary between an endurance athlete and a power athlete, for example a marathon runner and a hammer thrower.

Links to other units

You can find further information on this topic in Units R043, R044, R045 and R046.

Read about it

Read sample learner responses to applying the principles of training and see what examiners have said about these responses:

www.ocr.org.uk/Images/182635-applying-principles-of-training.pdf

Learn more about the FITTA principles:

www.netdoctor.co.uk/healthy-living/fitness/a12017/weekend-warriors-get-more-out-of-your-gym-visits

Assessment preparation

Think about the tasks that your teacher may set you to assess your knowledge of the principles of training. Make sure you:

- know what the principles of training are and can relate them to different activities
- are clear about what is meant by:
  - ○ progressive overload
  - ○ specificity
  - ○ reversibility/regression
  - ○ moderation
  - ○ variance.

How will you demonstrate the application of each of these to different sporting activities?

Mark scheme

L01 Know the principles of training in a sporting context		
Mark band 1	Mark band 2	Mark band 3
Outlines **most** of the principles of training with a **few** examples.	Describes **most** of the principles of training with a **range** of **relevant** examples.	Describes **all** of the principles of training with a **range** of **developed** examples which are applied to **specific** sporting contexts.

LO2 Know how training methods target different fitness components

Aerobic and anaerobic exercise

As we have already established, training programmes should follow the principles of training and be appropriate for each individual and the activity in which they take part. When designing an appropriate training programme, one simple consideration is whether the activity being trained for is **aerobic** or **anaerobic** (although it is possible for an activity to involve both aerobic and anaerobic energy use).

Difference between aerobic and anaerobic exercise

The difference between aerobic and anaerobic exercise is determined by how energy is predominantly being made within the body. The body's preferred way of making energy is to use oxygen, combining it with glucose (consumed via foodstuffs). The body does have a way to make energy when it does not have enough oxygen available, however. This is known as working anaerobically.

Aerobic exercise involves utilising oxygen to fuel the body. In other words, the body has enough oxygen available to meet the energy demands of that activity. This generally means that the energy demands and exercise intensity are relatively low, working at a steady rate. Aerobic exercise tends to be long, involving repetitive movements and making use of large muscle groups. The heart and **lungs** work productively to supply a suitable amount of oxygen to the working muscles. Examples of aerobic exercise include low-intensity cycling, running, swimming and rowing.

As exercise intensity increases, oxygen consumption cannot meet the demands of the exercise and the body has to revert to working anaerobically.

Anaerobic exercise involves fuelling the body without using oxygen. In simple terms, the body does not have enough oxygen and has to make energy in a different way. Glucose (from foodstuffs) is still broken down but without the use of oxygen. Energy demands and exercise intensity may be relatively high and the body may be working hard for a short period of time. Examples of anaerobic exercise include sprinting and lifting heavy weights.

Key terms

Aerobic With oxygen.

Aerobic exercise Using oxygen to produce energy during low-intensity, long-duration exercise.

Lungs Large spongy organs in the chest used for gas exchange.

Anaerobic Without oxygen.

Anaerobic exercise Not using oxygen to produce energy during high-intensity, short-duration exercise.

Figure 2.6 Sprinting is a high-intensity activity; oxygen would not be able to meet the energy demands, therefore sprinting is anaerobic

Figure 2.7 Tennis can involve playing a very long match, which means oxygen must be used to work aerobically; when the player sprints for the ball, however, exercise intensity will be high and energy will be made anaerobically

Methods of training aerobically and anaerobically

Aerobic training tends to be done over a long duration and carried out at a relatively low intensity. It often involves repeated movements of the arms and legs. The person training continues to consume appropriate levels of oxygen throughout the exercise. Examples include:

- walking
- jogging
- swimming
- rowing
- cycling
- cross-country skiing.

Aerobic training helps to improve the endurance (long-distance) capabilities of a performer.

Anaerobic training tends to be performed in short, fast bursts. The intensity level is increased to the point at which oxygen consumption cannot fully meet the energy demands. Although energy can still be made, the body also makes waste products, including lactic acid, which eventually prevents the muscles from functioning normally. This is why the body cannot do anaerobic training for long periods of time. Examples of anaerobic training include:

- a set of repetitions when weightlifting
- short bursts of fast running/sprinting
- short, fast swims
- high-intensity work as part of a circuit
- short track speed skating.

Anaerobic training helps to build speed, power and strength but can also help to improve endurance performance through high-intensity interval training (HIIT). This involves high-intensity work interspersed with periods of rest.

Components of fitness

There are many components of fitness, all of which can be developed by following an appropriately designed training programme. Different activities need different combinations of components of fitness to be developed. For example, team sports such as football, rugby, hockey and netball all require a combination of cardiovascular endurance, muscular endurance, speed, agility, strength and power.

Strength

Strength is defined as the extent to which a muscle or group of muscles can contract against resistance. The ability to contract

Figure 2.8 Jogging is a form of aerobic training; running at a lower intensity means that the body has enough oxygen and does not need to work anaerobically

Figure 2.9 Heavy weight training is a form of anaerobic training; gains in strength can be experienced by working at a high intensity with rest periods in between each set of weights

a muscles or muscle group against resistance can provide an advantage in many sporting contexts, for example:

- restraining an opponent in rugby
- holding a weight above your head in weightlifting
- pulling an oar through the water
- pushing a bobsleigh
- hitting a tennis ball hard when returning a serve.

Power

Power is defined as exerting muscular strength rapidly. This can be remembered as strength multiplied by speed. Power can provide an advantage in many sporting contexts, such as:

- pushing quickly out of the blocks in a sprint start
- punching an opponent quickly and with strength when boxing
- jumping up high in basketball to reach a rebound (leg power)
- releasing a javelin to maximise the length of the throw
- kicking a long conversion in rugby.

Agility

Agility is defined as the ability to move and change direction quickly while maintaining control. Agility is extremely important in many sporting contexts, such as:

- weaving between poles when performing a slalom run in skiing
- changing direction quickly to intercept a tennis shot from your opponent
- changing direction while sprinting to evade an opponent in rugby; this could be a side step
- changing direction quickly when dribbling with a football to avoid being tackled
- changing direction quickly when receiving then distributing the ball in basketball.

Balance

Balance is defined as the ability to maintain an upright or stable position. This generally involves maintaining the centre of mass over the base of support, although balance can also be dynamic, that is, maintaining balance while moving. The ability to maintain a stable position is particularly important in sporting contexts such as:

- holding a handstand or headstand in gymnastics
- holding a particular position when dancing
- balancing on the edge of the platform when high diving.

Flexibility

Flexibility is defined as the ability to move joints through an ample range of motion. A performer with a wide range of motion can often

Key terms

Power Exerting muscular strength rapidly.

Agility The ability to move and change direction quickly while maintaining control.

Balance The ability to maintain a stable position; this often involves maintaining the centre of mass over the base of support.

Figure 2.10 Agility is needed when playing netball to change direction at speed, for example when dodging away from an opponent to find space

Figure 2.11 Many gymnastics balances show the need to maintain a stable position; this can be seen when performing a headstand, handstand or arabesque

execute the desired technique or place themselves into a position that provides them with an advantage. Examples of how flexibility can help performers in a sporting context include:

- performing the splits in gymnastics
- a goalkeeper reaching high for a cross in football
- being able to perform the butterfly arm technique in swimming
- being able to perform a straddle or pike shape when trampolining
- being able to perform a full overhead serve in tennis.

Muscular endurance

Muscular endurance is defined as the ability of muscles to keep contracting repeatedly. This is often linked to aerobic events where repeated contractions take place at a steady state. Examples of sports in which muscular endurance can help performance over a long period of time include:

- cycling
- jogging
- rowing
- swimming
- walking
- cross-country skiing.

Cardiovascular endurance

Cardiovascular endurance is defined as the ability of the heart, lungs and blood vessels to get oxygen to the muscles and the ability of the body to use that oxygen. If the performer's body can supply oxygen to the muscles in suitable quantities as intensity levels increase, the performer is deemed to have excellent cardiovascular endurance. Cardiovascular endurance is important for endurance (long-duration) events, so it provides an advantage for performers in sporting contexts such as:

- long-distance running
- long-distance swimming
- cross-country skiing
- team games such as football, rugby, hockey and netball
- long-distance cycling.

Specific training methods for each of the fitness components

As mentioned previously, different sporting activities require performers to develop appropriate levels of fitness in the components needed for that activity. It is therefore important that performers know how to develop levels of fitness in specific components by taking part in specific methods of training.

Key terms

Muscular endurance The ability of muscles to keep contracting repeatedly.

Cardiovascular endurance The ability of the heart, lungs and blood vessels to get oxygen to the muscles and the ability of the body to use that oxygen.

Figure 2.12 Rugby matches last 80 minutes; performers therefore require good cardiovascular endurance in order to make energy aerobically for the duration of the match

Group activity

List ten different sporting activities and try to state which components of fitness are required for each of them.

Cardiovascular training

Training to improve cardiovascular endurance tends to take the form of steady state continuous training, interval training or fartlek training. The main reasons for choosing one of these methods are outlined below.

- **Continuous training** involves any activity or exercise that can be continuously repeated without suffering undue fatigue. This can include running, walking, cycling, rowing or swimming. Continuous training involves working at a constant rate or intensity and improves cardiovascular endurance. It is commonly referred to as 'steady state exercise'.

When completed correctly, continuous training improves the body's ability to use oxygen. The aerobic energy system therefore also improves. To carry this out, performers tend to use their heart rate as a guide, working in their aerobic training zone. The aerobic training zone can be calculated in the following way:

- ○ Estimate your maximum heart rate by subtracting your age from 220.
- ○ The aerobic training zone is 60–80 per cent of the maximum heart rate.

For example, if the participant is 16:

220 – 16 = 204

60 per cent of 204 = 122

80 per cent of 204 = 163

Therefore, work between 122 and 163 beats per minute.

- **Interval training** is a term for any training that involves periods of work and rest. The length of the work periods and rest periods determine which components of fitness are being trained. The amount of work and rest is often written as a ratio, known as the work-to-rest ratio (work : rest). Recent research has suggested that periods of high-intensity work with periods of rest can result in aerobic as well as anaerobic improvements. High-intensity interval training (HIIT) commonly involves a 2 : 1 work-to-rest ratio, for example 30 seconds of high-intensity work with 15 seconds rest, repeated up to six times.

- **Fartlek training** is known as 'speed play' and generally involves running, combining continuous and interval training. Fartlek is generally used to improve a performer's cardiovascular endurance. This type of training has more variety than continuous training, however, as the speed and intensity are varied.

Fartlek training typically involves running for approximately 30–60 minutes, during which time:

- ○ the speed of running is altered, for example sprint, jog, walk, jog, sprint
- ○ the terrain on which the running takes place is altered, for example running on flat roads, running up hills

Figure 2.13 Long-distance cycling can be an effective form of continuous training to improve cardiovascular endurance when working in the aerobic training zone

🔑 Key terms

Continuous training Any activity or exercise that can be continuously repeated without suffering undue fatigue.

Interval training Any training that involves periods of work and rest.

Fartlek training 'Speed play', which generally involves running, combining continuous and interval training.

○ the intensity of the run is changed, as this can allow the aerobic and anaerobic energy systems to be trained, for example sprinting will work the anaerobic system.

Fartlek is an effective form of training for team games, as constantly changing intensity mimics the demands of the game; for example in hockey, performers may walk, jog or sprint throughout the duration of a game.

Group activity

In pairs, try to think of a sport in which a performer would benefit from carrying out fartlek training. Report back to the rest of the class how fartlek could be designed to match the demands of the chosen sport.

Key term

Resistance training
Training that involves working against some kind of force that 'resists' your movement.

Resistance training

Resistance training involves working against some kind of force that opposes or 'resists' your movement. Weight training is the most common form of resistance training, although the resistance can also be as a result of body weight, pulling objects, working resistance bands or pulling your body through water.

Figure 2.14 Weight training in a fitness suite using a resistance machine

Resistance from machines in a weights gym involves a pulley system, whereby the weight is pulled as it resists your movement due to gravity. The contraction of the muscle as the weight is being lifted helps to develop strength and co-ordination. It is very important that the correct technique is used and that the person performing does not bend their back or put strain on vulnerable body parts. A suitable weight that can be lifted correctly should be used initially before further weight is added. This is known as progressive overload. It is vital that the correct technique is used and that a suitable posture is maintained.

Resistance training in a fitness suite can also involve lifting 'free weights', which are not attached to a resistance machine. Free weights such as dumb-bells or barbells are slightly harder, as the movement is controlled entirely by the person lifting them. The performer can add or reduce the weight on the bar as they

Figure 2.15 A spotter being used to prevent accident or injury for the person carrying out weight training

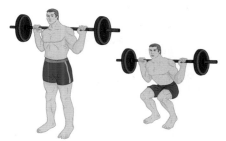

Figure 2.16 A performer using a free weight (barbell) to perform squats to train the leg muscles

wish, and can make use of a weights bench if they need support. Performers may need a 'spotter' for very heavy weights, to ensure they do not get caught under the weight. The spotter can act as 'insurance' – if the weight cannot be lifted, the spotter can make sure it does not drop onto the person lifting it.

One repetition of a weight is the completion of one lift or pull of that weight. Performers tend to adjust the number of repetitions they do to control what adaptation in their body they achieve. A 'set' of repetitions is a group of repetitions that should be completed before having a rest period. As an example, a performer may complete three or four sets of 15 repetitions with a light weight to improve muscular endurance and the tone of the muscles.

Table 2.2 Examples of resistance training programmes

Aim	Programme
To improve muscular endurance and muscle tone	Low-intensity (light) weights ● high number of repetitions (12–15) ● high number of sets (3–5 sets)
To improve strength and muscle bulk/hypertrophy	High-intensity (heavy) weights ● low number of repetitions (4–8) ● low number of sets (1–3 sets)

Resistance training can be done as part of a **circuit**. In this form of training, the performer carries out different exercises at various stations. The exercises can involve resistance from weights or from your own body weight. Resistance provided via your own body weight can provide strength gains and increase the size of muscles. This is called muscular **hypertrophy**. Examples include press-ups and sit-ups. An example circuit is shown in Figure 2.17.

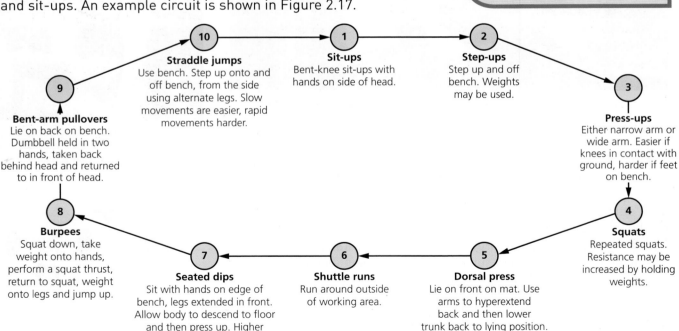

Figure 2.17 An example circuit, which includes some resistance exercises

Figure 2.18 A press-up is an example of resistance training using body weight that can be included in a circuit

Power training

One of the main ways to increase strength and speed (power) is through **plyometric training**. Plyometric training involves taking part in repeated exercises such as bounding, hopping or jumping over hurdles to create fast, powerful movements, but it can also include 'jump and clap' press-ups or medicine ball work. The exercises make use of the elastic properties of muscle fibres. An example of how plyometrics can work is shown below:

1 The athlete jumps off a box.
2 As they land, their **quadriceps** lengthen (**eccentric contraction**).
3 This stores 'elastic energy', which can be released through a further immediate jump.
4 The second jump (using the stored elastic energy) makes use of a stronger **concentric contraction**.
5 Thus the eccentric contraction has caused a stronger concentric contraction.

Group activity

Design a circuit training plan for the rest of the class to carry out. Ensure that the circuit includes some resistance activities.

Key terms

Plyometric training Repeated exercises such as bounding, hopping or jumping over hurdles designed to create fast, powerful movements.

Quadriceps Muscles at the front of the upper leg that straighten the leg.

Eccentric contraction Where the muscle lengthens while contracting.

Concentric contraction Where the muscle shortens while contracting.

Figure 2.19 Performer using box jumping to increase power in the leg muscles

Interval training is often used to increase power and/or cardiovascular endurance. The performer carries out short, high-intensity periods of work to near maximal effort, then has a short period of rest before another period of high-intensity work. This can involve sprints, use of weights, cycling and so on. When the interval training involves very high-intensity periods of work, it is often known as high-intensity interval training (HIIT).

Acceleration sprint training is another type of interval training. In this type of training, the athlete sprints at maximal (or near to maximal) effort for a short period of time, before having a period of rest. After the rest, the performer carries out another work period. This is repeated until the number of sprint sets are completed.

Flexibility training

Static stretching is perhaps the most common way to increase flexibility. It involves stretches being held to increase the range of movement possible at a joint. Static stretches can be either active or passive:

- **Active stretching** involves the participant (only) being in control of the stretch, with no external force involved (for example the ground or a partner). An active stretch requires the participant to actively stretch their joint. This stretch is produced from the opposing muscle group/s. Examples of active stretches are shown in Figures 2.20 and 2.21.

Key term

Static stretching Holding stretches, either actively or passively, to increase the range of movement at a joint.

Figure 2.20 Lifting the leg from the floor and moving the toes up towards the tibia to stretch the muscles in the leg

Figure 2.21 Leaning sideways to stretch the side of the top half of the body (external obliques)

- **Passive stretching** involves the use of an external force to create the stretch. This can come from a partner, a resistance band or gravity. The participant themselves may pull the stretch further and act as the 'external force'. Some examples are shown in Figures 2.22, 2.23 and 2.24.

Figure 2.22 Participant acting as the force to create the passive stretch

Figure 2.23 Partner being used to create the passive stretch

Dynamic stretching is slightly different to static stretching in that while it takes the body through the range of motion, the stretch is not held for any length of time: the range of motion is experienced within the movement being completed. Examples of dynamic stretches include:

- ankle rotations
- lunges
- neck twists
- arm circles
- bringing the knees up when running.

Figure 2.24 Resistance band being used to create the passive stretch

Dynamic stretches can be incorporated into pre-activity warm ups to get the body used to the range of motion that will be experienced in the activity itself.

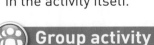
Group activity

Try out some of the active, passive and dynamic stretches discussed in this chapter.

Although all stretching is beneficial for flexibility (the range of movement at a joint), static stretches tend to be used more to improve flexibility. Dynamic stretches, on the other hand, tend to be more about preparing the joint for movements and preventing injury during the activity.

Agility training

The most common form of training to develop agility is called SAQ (speed, agility, quickness) training. This training aims to use explosive actions which involve changing direction quickly to reprogramme the neuromuscular system to work more effectively. SAQ training can involve:

- sprinting through ladders – involving landing on the balls of your feet; one set of this type of exercise generally involves moving down the 'ladder' quickly with light feet before moving back up again
- agility hurdles – used in a variety of ways; the participant sprints and changes direction while showing quick feet over the hurdles
- sprinting to cones in different directions – often with a common start point; the participant sprints to sets of cones and returns to the start point each time
- retrieval of objects in different directions – often with a common start point; the participant is challenged to retrieve objects from different points and place them back at the start point.

Participants may perform SAQ training on its own or include it as part of a circuit. If, for example, a participant wanted to improve both their strength and agility, they might design a circuit that includes strengthening and agility tasks.

Balance training

On occasions, participants may wish to train to improve their balance. Although balance is an inherited ability, it can be improved by building strength in your core as well as in the lower and upper body. This allows a stronger base to control the balance. This strength is generally improved by taking part in balance exercises, including using:

- balance boards – the participant works on maintaining their balance on a wobbling board
- exercise balls – many balance exercises make use of an exercise ball; some examples include:
  - seated ball balance – sitting on the ball with a straight back, one leg is slowly lifted off the floor for a few seconds while the participant aims to maintain their balance
  - ball walks – sitting on the ball, with hands down on the ball and back straight, the participant aims to walk the feet forward; the participant contracts their stomach muscles (**abdominals**); as they walk forward, their back slowly rolls down the ball until their shoulders are in contact with the ball and they can make a 'bridge' position. Generally, this is repeated 10–15 times. It is extremely challenging for balance and core strength.

Read about it

Learn more about using an exercise ball:

www.verywellfit.com/ball-workout-for-balance-and-strength-1230908

Read about it

Learn more about agility ladders:

www.agilityladders.net

Key term

Abdominals Stomach muscles that protect internal organs.

Figure 2.25 Using an exercise ball to work on balance

Table 2.3 Training methods and the fitness components they improve

Training type	Main fitness component improved	Other fitness components that can be improved in combination
Cardiovascular training, e.g. steady state (continuous), interval, fartlek	Cardiovascular endurance	All cardiovascular training improves muscular endurance Interval training can improve aerobic and anaerobic capabilities Interval training can also increase power and speed Fartlek training can help to increase speed and power
Resistance training, e.g. resistance machines, free weights, circuits	Strength	Lighter resistance can help to increase muscular endurance
Power training, e.g. interval, plyometrics, repetition and acceleration sprint	Power	Interval training improves cardiovascular endurance Acceleration sprint training can increase speed
Flexibility training, e.g. static (passive and active), dynamic	Flexibility	Dynamic stretching can help to increase power
Agility training, e.g. agility ladder, agility hurdles	Agility	Agility training can help to increase speed and co-ordination, while improving balance on the move (dynamic balance)
Balance training, e.g. balance board, exercise ball	Balance	Balance training helps to develop strength

💬 Classroom discussion

Discuss the positives and negatives of taking part in the following training types:

- continuous training
- resistance training using free weights
- plyometric training
- flexibility training using static stretches
- balance training using an exercise ball.

Can you think of an equal number of positives and negatives for each training type (for example in continuous training, jogging, can be tedious but does not necessarily require much equipment)?

Stretch activity

1 Match the components of fitness with different training methods.

2 Choose a sporting example, for example football (which requires cardiovascular endurance, muscular endurance, power, agility, strength, speed and balance), and describe the best combination of training types to use for this sport.

Group activity

Design a resistance training session to try out with a partner. You could use free weights, resistance machines or your own body weight. Think carefully about how many sets and repetitions to do. Remember that:

- strength involves:
  ○ high-intensity (heavy) weights
  ○ low number of repetitions (4–8)
  ○ low number of sets (1–3 sets)
- muscular endurance involves:
  ○ low-intensity (light) weights
  ○ high number of repetitions (12–15)
  ○ high number of sets (3–5 sets)

Links to other units

You can find further information on this topic in Units R043, R044, R045 and R046.

Know it!

1 Describe what aerobic and anaerobic exercise are.

2 State different training methods that can improve aerobic and/or anaerobic fitness.

3 Name the different components of fitness.

4 Explain how different training types can improve different components of fitness.

Read about it

Resistance training:

www.bodybuilding.com/fun/beginners-guide-to-resistance-training.html

A guide to fartlek training:

www.realbuzz.com/articles-interests/running/article/your-guide-to-fartlek-training

Balance training:

www.power-systems.com/shop/category/balance-training?lastRowID=20

Using interval training for cardiovascular endurance:

www.sportsrec.com/99278-increasing-aerobic-fitness-interval.html

Assessment preparation

Think about the tasks that your teacher may set you to assess your knowledge of training methods. Make sure you:

- know what the components of fitness are
- are clear about what is meant by:
  - ○ cardiovascular training
  - ○ resistance training
  - ○ power training
  - ○ flexibility training
  - ○ agility training
  - ○ balance training.

How will you demonstrate how each of these training methods can be used to improve certain fitness components?

How will you demonstrate that you understand how training methods can be used to target a combination of fitness components?

Mark scheme

LO2: Know how training methods target different fitness components		
Mark band 1	Mark band 2	Mark band 3
Outlines aerobic and anaerobic exercise supported with a **few** examples of training methods. Identifies **some** of the components of fitness and a **limited range** of specific training methods which target them.	**Describes** aerobic and anaerobic exercise supported with **some relevant** examples of training methods. Identifies **some** of the components of fitness and describes **a range** of specific training methods and how they can target fitness components, both individually and in combination.	**Comprehensively describes** aerobic and anaerobic exercise supported with a **wide range** of **relevant** examples of training methods. Identifies **most** of the components of fitness and describes a **wide range** of specific training methods and how they can target fitness components, both individually and in combination.

L03 Be able to conduct fitness tests

Before designing a suitable training programme, it is common for athletes to take part in a range of fitness tests. This is important to:

- identify the strengths and weaknesses of the athlete
- inform what the training programme should include
- compare the athlete's fitness scores to national averages
- provide a benchmark figure to refer to after training, to monitor if improvement has taken place.

Tests that assess fitness

When completing a range of fitness tests, it is important to ensure that several guidelines are followed:

- Tests should be completed according to the designated protocols and guidelines set down by the fitness industry. If the protocol is not followed, then the **validity** of the test will be compromised (a fitness test is valid if it tests the component of fitness that it aims to test). Although there are many different fitness tests available, it is important that the correct protocol is followed meticulously to ensure that test results are valid and can be compared to standardised national averages. Using the correct equipment for a test helps to ensure its validity, for example a sit-and-reach flexibility board, a CD recording for a multistage fitness test (bleep test), or a wall ruler for a vertical jump test.

Figure 2.26 Fitness testing

Getting started

As a class, discuss what fitness tests you have completed in your lives:
- Can you remember the names of the tests?
- Can you describe how the tests were completed?
- Can you remember your scores?
- Which tests were easier/ harder than others?

Key term

Validity A fitness test is valid if it tests the component of fitness that it aims to test.

Links to other units

You will find the information in R041 to be very important to safely conduct fitness tests.

- When preparing for fitness tests, the administrator may need to decide whether the participant needs to be medically assessed before taking part, to ensure they are physically capable of completing the test or tests. Sometimes a medical questionnaire can be given prior to testing to establish this.

- Many tests are **maximal tests**, meaning that they require maximal effort in order to produce a valid, comparable result, for example the 12-minute Cooper run. Participants with high blood pressure or heart problems may therefore be advised not to take part in tests that are too demanding. **Sub-maximal tests** do not require maximal effort to gain a valid result, for example the Harvard step test.

- Participants must fully warm up prior to testing. They should also be briefed on the appropriate protocol of how to do each test, as if protocol is not followed, the validity of the test will be compromised.

- It is important to ensure that the tests completed are reliable. **Reliability** means that a test can be repeated and give similar results if it is carried out in the same way each time. In simple terms, the conditions of the test must always be identical so that it is most likely that the same results will be produced.

Testing sequence

When repeating a range of fitness tests to work out if improvement (progression or regression) has occurred, the validity of the results will be better if the tests are always carried out in the same order.

Tests for each component of fitness

Strength tests

Burpee squat thrust and jump test

A **burpee** is sometimes called a squat thrust and jump. The burpee test is a test of **strength endurance** – the ability to apply strength in activities that have an element of endurance. The burpee test also involves the use of balance, co-ordination and body control. As the burpee squat thrusts are done over a period of time, the participant will not necessarily work at maximal effort, therefore the test is sub-maximal.

- **Equipment**: non-slip cushioned surface to perform the test on and a stopwatch.
- **Protocol to follow to ensure validity and reliability**:
  - To start the burpee test, the participant must stand up straight (erect) with their arms by their sides.
  - From this starting/standing position, the participant is required to squat down and place their hands on the floor, just in front of their feet.
  - The participant should then lean forward slightly to move their body weight onto their hands.

Key terms

Maximal tests Fitness tests that require maximal effort in order to produce a valid, comparable result.

Sub-maximal tests Fitness tests that do not require maximal effort to gain a valid result.

Reliability A fitness test is reliable if it can be repeated and gives similar results each time.

Burpee A squat thrust and jump.

Strength endurance Ability to apply strength in activities that have an element of endurance (a long duration).

Group activity

In pairs, and with the permission and supervision of a suitably qualified adult, have a go at guiding your partner through some of the fitness tests outlined in this chapter. Ensure their validity and reliability by following the stated protocol correctly. Once completed, record your partner's results neatly so you can interpret how well they have done.

- ○ At this point, the legs should be thrust back quickly to place the participant in a press-up position.
- ○ Some burpee tests require you to perform a press-up (push-up) at this point.
- ○ The participant's back should be straight in the press-up position.
- ○ Once this position is completed, the legs should be pulled forwards and placed back into the squat position, before jumping up into the standing position again.
- ○ One full and complete burpee is from the erect standing position back to the erect standing position.

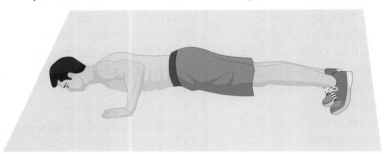

Figure 2.27 The press-up position during the burpee strength endurance test

- **Scoring**: The score recorded is the number of burpees completed over a fixed period of time. The Spartan SGX Fitness Test lasts for up to five minutes. Participants can choose to do as many burpees as they can in 30 seconds up to five minutes. For this test, the chest must touch the ground during the press-up and the feet must leave the ground when returning to the standing position with the hands reaching up past the ears. The test can be repeated and the best score used.

  The ultimate score, known as being 'Spartan Fit', is for adults to complete over 80 (women) or 85 (men) in five minutes. A good result for a 30-second test attempt is to complete more than 16 burpees for men and 12 for women.

Table 2.4 Burpees completed over five minutes comparison chart

Men								
Age	4–8	9–13	14–19	20–29	30–39	40–49	50–59	60+
Spartan Fit	55	60	83	85	83	78	75	70
Healthy	40	45	68	70	68	63	60	55
Poor	25	30	53	55	53	48	45	40
Very poor	<25	<30	<53	<55	<53	<48	<45	<40
Women								
Age	4–8	9–13	14–19	20–29	30–39	40–49	50–59	60+
Spartan Fit	55	60	73	80	75	70	67	62
Healthy	40	45	58	65	60	55	52	47
Poor	25	30	43	50	45	40	37	32
Very poor	<25	<30	<43	<50	<45	<40	<37	<32

Squat test

A 'squat' involves standing up straight with your hands by your sides or horizontally extended out in front of you. As you squat down, bending your knees, the angle at your knees should reach 90 degrees (that is, sitting down on a chair position) before returning to the standing position. You perform as many squats as possible until you can do no more, so this is deemed a maximal test.

- **Equipment**: none, although the participant should be on a suitable non-slip surface; some participants use a chair or bench to guide how far down to squat, without actually fully sitting down.
- **Protocol to follow to ensure validity and reliability**:
  - The test simply involves completing a down and up squat action as many times as possible before fatigue stops you from doing any more.
  - Many participants complete this looking into a mirror and use a chair or bench to gauge where their 90-degree point is at their knees.
- **Scoring**: use Table 2.5 to gauge how well you perform in this test.

Figure 2.28 Participant completing a squat

Table 2.5 Squat test comparison chart

Men					
Age	20–29	30–39	40–49	50–59	60+
Excellent	>34	>32	>29	>26	>23
Good	33–4	30–2	27–9	24–6	21–3
Above average	30–2	27–9	24–6	21–3	18–20
Average	27–9	24–6	21–3	18–20	15–17
Below average	24–6	21–3	18–20	15–17	12–14
Poor	21–3	18–20	15–17	12–14	9–11
Very poor	<21	<18	<15	<12	<9
Women					
Age	20–29	30–39	40–49	50–59	60+
Excellent	>29	>26	>23	>20	>17
Good	27–9	24–6	21–3	18–20	15–17
Above average	24–6	21–3	18–20	15–17	12–14
Average	21–3	18–20	15–17	12–14	9–11
Below average	18–20	15–17	12–14	9–11	6–8
Poor	15–17	12–14	9–11	6–8	3–5
Very poor	<15	<12	<9	<6	<3

The wall squat (sit) test

The wall squat (or wall sit) test is a test of muscular strength and strength endurance. You simply hold a sitting position against a wall (with one foot off the floor) until you cannot hold the position any longer. This is a maximal test as it is to exhaustion.

Figure 2.29 Performing the wall squat test

- **Equipment**: a wall to lean against and a stopwatch.
- **Protocol to follow to ensure validity and reliability**:
  - The participant adopts a sitting position against a wall.
  - The participant's back should be flat on the wall and their knees should be at 90 degrees.
  - When ready, the participant lifts one foot off the floor (approximately 5 cm) and the time starts.
  - The participant stays in this position for as long as possible.
  - They can repeat the test using their other leg.
- **Scoring**: the test is timed; the score is the time recorded.

Table 2.6 Normative data comparison scores for the wall squat test

Rating	Men (seconds)	Women (seconds)
Excellent	>100	>60
Good	75–100	45–60
Average	50–74	35–44
Below average	25–49	20–34
Poor	<25	<20

Power tests

Vertical jump test

The vertical jump test is also known as the 'sergeant jump test'. It is a test of leg power. It is a maximal test, as the participant needs to jump as high as they can with maximum force.

- **Equipment**: wall ruler/slider and chalk.
- **Protocol to follow to ensure validity and reliability**:
  - The participant starts with feet flat, beside the wall.
  - They stand and push the wall ruler with their fingertips as high as possible.
  - They can now see where their 'zero point' is, depending on how high they pushed the ruler.
  - At this point they should apply chalk (or something else to make a mark) to their fingertips.
  - From a standing position, the participant now jumps as high as possible, marking the wall ruler with the chalk on their fingertips.

Classroom discussion

Having completed the wall squat test, discuss which foot (right or left) tended to score the best. Are there any obvious reasons for this?

Figure 2.30 Completing the vertical jump test

- **Scoring**: the height jumped is recorded in centimeters. Use Table 2.7 to gauge how well you performed in this test.

Table 2.7 Comparison scores from the vertical jump test

Rating	Men (cm)	Women (cm)
Excellent	>70	>60
Very good	61–70	51–60
Above average	51–60	41–50
Average	41–50	31–40
Below average	31–40	21–30
Poor	21–30	11–20
Very poor	<21	<11

Standing long jump test

The standing long jump test is often called the 'broad jump test'. It is a test of leg power. It is a maximal test, as the participant has to jump as far as possible with maximal force.

- **Equipment**: non-slip surface on which to land (could be sand or a mat) and a tape measure to assess distance jumped.
- **Protocol to follow to ensure validity and reliability**:
  - The participant should stand behind a clearly marked line.
  - Feet should be slightly apart.
  - The participant can rock on their feet and swing their arms to gain momentum.
  - The participant jumps forwards as far as they can, landing on both feet.
  - Measurement is taken at the point where both feet landed.

- **Scoring**: the score is recorded in centimetres and compared to national average tables.

Figure 2.31 Participant completing the standing long jump test

Table 2.8 Comparative scoring table for the standing long jump test

Rating	Men (cm)	Women (cm)
Excellent	>250	>200
Very good	241–50	191–200
Above average	231–40	181–90
Average	221–30	171–80
Below average	211–20	161–70
Poor	191–210	141–60
Very poor	<191	<141

Agility tests

30 ft agility shuttle run test

This test is one example of a number of possible agility shuttle run tests. It tests the agility and speed of the participant. The validity of the test is sometimes questioned, as it could be perceived to be more about the speed of running than the agility required to turn. It is occasionally amended to become the 10 m agility shuttle run test. As this test is run at maximum intensity/speed, it is a maximal test.

- **Equipment**: wooden blocks, cones (markers), tape measure and a stopwatch.
- **Protocol to follow to ensure validity and reliability**:
  - Two set points are set up and marked, 30 ft apart.
  - Two wooden blocks are placed at one end.
  - On the command of 'go', the participant starts at the end opposite the blocks and sprints towards the blocks, picking one of them up and returning to the original start point.
  - The participant runs back to collect the second block and returns to the start point, running through the finish line, at which point the clock stops.
- **Scoring**: the time is recorded. The participant may try the test up to three times to increase the reliability; their best score should be used.
- Go to page 8 of **http://www.newton.k12.in.us/hs/pe/images/ physical-fitness-guide.pdf** where you need to use the 85th and 50th percentile boxes that relate to boys and girls for the 'shuttle test'.

Illinois agility run test

This is probably the most well-known test of agility. The test involves running around cones and is simple and easy to set up. It is completed as fast as possible and is therefore a maximal test.

- **Equipment**: cones/markers, stopwatch and a tape measure to measure the distance between cones.
- **Protocol to follow to ensure validity and reliability**:
  - The cones should be set out as shown in Figure 2.32.
  - The participant should start facing down flat on the floor.
  - On the command of 'go', the participant should run around the cones as shown in Figure 2.32 as fast as possible.
- **Scoring**: the time taken to complete the test is recorded in seconds. Use Table 2.9 to gauge how well you performed in this test.

Table 2.9 Comparison scores for the Illinois agility run test

Rating	Men (seconds)	Women (seconds)
Excellent	<15.2	<17.0
Above average	15.2–16.1	17.0–17.9
Average	16.2–18.1	18.0–21.7
Below average	18.2–19.3	21.8–23.0
Poor	>19.3	>23.0

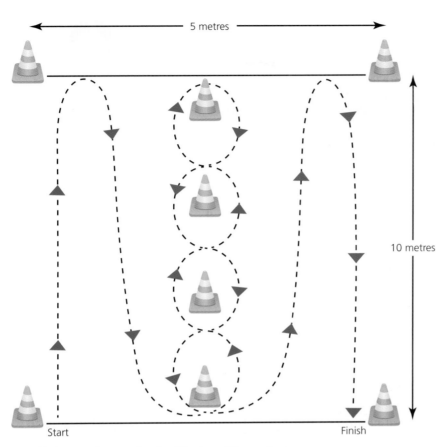

Figure 2.32 Set up of cones for the Illinois agility run test

Balance test

Standing stork test

This test measures static balance, that is, the ability to maintain a still position. It does not involve maximal exertion or work to exhaustion, so it is a sub-maximal test.

- **Equipment**: stopwatch.
- **Protocol to follow to ensure validity and reliability**:
  ○ The participant stands balanced on two flat feet with hands on hips.
  ○ One leg is lifted to a position whereby the toes of the lifted leg touch the inside of the knee of the stationary leg.
  ○ The timekeeper will then tell the participant to raise the heel of the planted leg (and the stopwatch should start).
  ○ The participant stays balanced on one leg for as long as possible.

- **Scoring**: the time is recorded in seconds until they lose balance or their toes are removed from the knee of the straight, stationary leg. Use Table 2.10 to gauge how well you performed in this test.

Table 2.10 Comparison scores for the standing stork test

Rating	Men (seconds)	Women (seconds)
Excellent	>50	>30
Above average	41–50	23–30
Average	31–40	16–22
Below average	20–30	10–15
Poor	<20	<10

Source: Johnson and Nelson (1979) Practical Measurements for Evaluation in Physical Education

Flexibility tests

Sit-and-reach test

The sit-and-reach test is a standard test of flexibility that is relatively simple to perform. The test is performed slowly and is therefore a sub-maximal test.

- **Equipment**: a sit-and-reach measurement board.
- **Protocol to follow to ensure validity and reliability**:
  - The participant should sit on the floor with both legs straight.
  - No shoes should be worn and the feet should be flat against the sit-and-reach board.
  - The slider (if available on the board) should be set to 14 cm, to be in line with the toes.
  - The participant should reach forward and push the slider as far as they can.
- **Scoring**: the score is recorded in centimetres. Use Table 2.11 to gauge how well you performed in this test.

Table 2.11 Comparison scores for the sit-and-reach test

Rating	Men (cm)	Women (cm)
Super	>27	>30
Excellent	17 to 27	21 to 30
Good	6 to 16	11 to 20
Average	0 to 5	1 to 10
Fair	−8 to −1	−7 to 0
Poor	−20 to −9	−15 to −8
Very poor	<−20	<−15

Figure 2.33 A participant completing the standing stork balance test

Figure 2.34 A participant completing the sit-and-reach test

Trunk flexion test

The trunk flexion test is a standard test of flexibility that is relatively simple to perform. It can be performed slowly and is therefore a sub-maximal test.

- **Equipment**: a metre rule.
- **Protocol to follow to ensure validity and reliability**:
  - No shoes should be worn for the test.
  - Having thoroughly warmed up, the participant sits down on the floor with legs extended and flat. Feet should be approximately 30 cm apart.
  - The person assisting with the test should place the rule on the floor between the participant's legs. The 38 cm mark should be level with the bottom of the participant's feet, so that the zero point is between their legs, counting up to 38 as it gets to the bottom of their feet.
  - When ready, the participant leans forward and slides their fingers along the rule as far as they can.
  - The person assisting measures and records how far the fingertips can reach down the rule.
  - You are generally allowed to repeat the test up to three times to increase reliability.
- **Scoring**: the biggest distance reached is recorded in centimetres. A good result is greater than 51 cm for men and greater than 56 cm for women.

Muscular endurance tests

30-second sit-up test

The aim of this test is to perform as many sit-ups as you can in 30 seconds. This is a maximal test, as the sit-ups are completed as fast as possible. The test measures muscular endurance of the abdominals and hip flexors.

- **Equipment**: stopwatch, comfortable mat and an observer/partner to count the sit-ups.
- **Protocol to follow to ensure validity and reliability**:
  - The participant lies on a mat with knees bent at 90 degrees and feet flat on the floor.
  - Feet can be held down by a partner.
  - On the command of 'go', the stopwatch starts and the participant begins to complete as many full sit-ups as they can.
  - The upper body should be vertical at the top of the sit-up, before returning to the floor.
- **Scoring**: the number of sit-ups completed in 30 seconds can be compared to Table 2.12.

Table 2.12 Normative data for the 30-second sit-up test

Rating	Men (number of sit-ups)	Women (number of sit-ups)
Excellent	>30	>25
Above average	26–30	21–25
Average	20–25	15–20
Below average	17–19	9–14
Poor	<17	<9

Figure 2.35 Participant completing the 30-second sit-up test

One-minute press-up (push-up) test

The one-minute press-up test measures upper body strength and strength endurance. There are many variations of this test. It is a maximal test, as you continue to do press-ups until you are incapable of doing any more.

- **Equipment**: non-slip mat.
- **Protocol to follow to ensure validity and reliability**:
  - The participant starts in a press-up position. The back should be straight and the arms fully extended 90 degrees to the body. Hands should be shoulder-width apart and feet slightly apart.
  - The test starts when the participant moves down to a predetermined point or to touch an object with their chest. This can be another person's clenched fist in contact with the floor.
  - When they rise back to the starting position, they have completed one press-up.
- **Scoring**: the score is how many full press-ups are completed in a minute.

Table 2.13 Normative data for the one-minute press-up test (full push-ups for men, kneeling push-ups for women)

Age	20–29		30–39		40–49		50–59		60+	
	Men	Women	Men	Women	Men	Women	Men	Women	Men	Women
Excellent	>54	>48	>44	>39	>39	>34	>34	>29	>29	>19
Good	45–54	34–48	35–44	25–39	30–39	20–34	25–34	15–29	20–29	5–19
Average	35–44	17–33	25–34	12–24	20–29	8–19	15–24	6–14	10–19	3–4
Poor	20–34	6–16	15–24	4–11	12–19	3–7	8–14	2–5	5–9	1–2
Very poor	<20	<6	<15	<4	<12	<3	<8	<2	<5	<1

Source: American College of Sports Medicine

Cardiovascular endurance tests

Cooper run

The Cooper run is a test of cardiovascular endurance in which the participant simply runs as far as they can in 12 minutes. It is a maximal test.

- **Equipment**: flat or oval running track, stopwatch and a recording sheet for scores.
- **Protocol to follow to ensure validity and reliability**:
  - Cones are laid out or a track is prepared to allow the distance covered to be measured.
  - The participant starts to run when commanded to do so.
  - The participant runs as far as they can in the 12-minute time period.
  - The participant can walk if they need to but should be encouraged to run as far as possible to exhaustion.
- **Scoring**: the distance run is recorded in metres. This can be used to predict what score would be achieved in a VO_2 max test.
  - Go to **https://www.ptdirect.com/training-delivery/client-assessment/cooper-12-minute-run-a-predictive-test-of-vo2max** to see the normative data scores for the 12-minute Cooper run.

Harvard step test

The Harvard step test is a sub-maximal test of aerobic fitness.

- **Equipment**: basic gym bench (approximately 50 cm high), stopwatch, metronome and Harvard step test recording CD.
- **Protocol to follow to ensure validity and reliability**:
  - The participant starts facing the bench, standing up.
  - When ready, an observer starts the metronome at the desired speed (30 ticks per minute) so that the participant can hear it clearly.
  - When ready, the participant starts to step up onto and down from the bench in time with the metronome for five minutes or until exhaustion.
  - The observer stops the test after five minutes and the participant should sit on the bench.

- ○ The observer should measure the participant's heart rate (beats per minute, or bpm) one minute after finishing the test – this is pulse 1.
- ○ The observer should measure the participant's heart rate (bpm) two minutes after finishing the test – this is pulse 2.
- ○ The observer should measure the participant's heart rate (bpm) three minutes after finishing the test – this is pulse 3.
- **Scoring**: an estimate of the participant's level of fitness can be determined from the three recorded pulses as follows:

Result = 30000 ÷ (pulse 1 + pulse 2 + pulse 3)

The result can be compared to **normative data**, such as those shown in Table 2.14.

Table 2.14 Normative data for the Harvard step test for 16 year olds

	Men	Women
Excellent	>90.0	>86.0
Above average	80.0–90.0	76.0–86.0
Average	65.0–79.9	61.0–75.9
Below average	55.0–64.9	50.0–60.9
Poor	<55	<50

Key term

Normative data Data from a reference population that establishes a baseline score or measurement, against which your score or measurement can be compared.

Multistage fitness test (bleep test)

The multistage fitness test (bleep test) is a maximal and progressive test of cardiovascular endurance. It is maximal in that the participant works to exhaustion, and progressive as it gets progressively harder.

- **Equipment**: cones, tape measure (20 m or more), CD with test and a sheet to record the score.
- **Protocol to follow to ensure validity and reliability**:
  - ○ Lay out cones or mark lines 20 m apart.
  - ○ The participant runs 20 m in time with the bleeps.
  - ○ As the levels go up (progress), the time between the bleeps gets shorter.
  - ○ The participant keeps running until they cannot keep up with the bleeps.

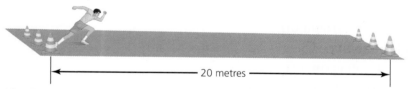
20 metres

Figure 2.36 Participant attempting the multistage fitness test (bleep test)

- **Scoring**: the score is recorded as a level and bleep reached (for example, level 9 bleep 3) and should be compared to the data in Table 2.15. The recorded score can be used to provide a prediction of an individual's VO_2 max.

Table 2.15 Normative data for the multistage fitness test (bleep test)
(L = level, S = shuttle number)

Men					
Age	**14–16**	**17–20**	**21–30**	**31–40**	**41–50**
Excellent	L12 S7	L12 S12	L12 S12	L11 S7	L10 S4
Above average	L11 S2	L11 S6	L11 S7	L10 S4	L9 S4
Average	L9 S9	L9 S2	L9 S3	L6 S10	L6 S9
Below average	L7 S1	L7 S6	L7 S8	L6 S7	L5 S9
Poor	<L6 S6	<L7 S2	<L7 S5	<L6 S4	<L5 S2
Women					
Age	**14–16**	**17–20**	**21–30**	**31–40**	**41–50**
Excellent	L10 S9	L10 S11	L10 S8	L10 S4	L9 S9
Above average	L9 S1	L9 S3	L9 S2	L8 S7	L7 S2
Average	L6 S7	L6 S8	L6 S2	L6 S3	L5 S7
Below average	L5 S1	L5 S2	L5 S1	L4 S6	L4 S2
Poor	<L4 S7	<L4 S9	<L4 S9	<L4 S5	<L4 S1

Tri-level aerobic test

The tri-level aerobic test is based on an ergometer (bicycle) and is usually carried out in a sports science lab.

- **Equipment**: an ergometer cycle machine (with workload dial), a stopwatch and scales to determine the body weight of the athlete prior to the test.
- **Protocol to follow to ensure validity and reliability**:
  - ○ The participant pedals in one-minute increments of 25 watts (starting at 25 watts) until their heart rate reaches 75 per cent of their predicted maximum heart rate (220 minus age).
  - ○ They continue pedalling until the end of the minute during which the target heart rate was reached.
- **Scoring**: scoring is rather complex. The workload at which the target heart rate is achieved is written down. This score is then divided by body weight. Normative scoring tables are available for comparison.

How to interpret the results of fitness tests

It is important that you can assess how well or otherwise testing has gone. One way to do this is to compare scores to the available normative data, that is, how do the outcomes compare to the average range achieved for the tests used? Some sample normative data has been provided for the tests above. Participants can see how they compare to averages and determine whether their 'classification' is improving.

Classroom discussion

Think about the knowledge you have gained about fitness tests and training methods. Discuss which components of fitness you feel would be the easiest to improve, that is, which you think would show the biggest improvements when tests are redone.

Stretch activity

1   Look at a partner's full set of results and try to interpret what has gone well or not so well. Give feedback to your partner on how well they completed the tests, referring to the normative data tables.

2   Choose two or three fitness tests in which you feel your own or another's results were slightly low. Start to design an appropriate training programme for these fitness components and think about when a retest (in the same order) should take place to see if there has been improvement.

Know it!

1   State the names of four fitness tests and outline what they aim to measure.

2   Describe the protocols for these tests so that they can be carried out in a valid way.

3   Define what is meant by the terms 'validity' and 'reliability'.

4   Describe how normative data tables are used.

5   Describe what training types could be used to improve the test scores of the four different fitness tests in question 1.

Read about it

Validity and reliability:

www.ptdirect.com/training-delivery/client-assessment/understanding-validity-and-reliability-in-fitness-testing

12-minute Cooper run test:

www.verywellfit.com/fitness-test-for-endurance-12-minute-run-3120264

Multistage fitness test (bleep test):

www.scienceforsport.com/multistage-fitness-beep-test

A guide to many of the fitness tests:

www.topendsports.com/testing

Multistage fitness test norms:

www.helpmeteach.co.uk/multi-stage-fitness-tests-scores-or-vo2-comparisons-r135

Assessment preparation

Think about the tasks that your teacher may set you to assess your knowledge of fitness testing. Make sure you:

- know how to carry out a range of fitness tests
- are clear about what is meant by:
  - reliability
  - validity
  - maximal tests
  - sub-maximal tests
  - normative data.

How will you demonstrate that you understand how to interpret the results of fitness testing?

Mark scheme

LO3: Be able to conduct fitness tests		
Mark band 1	Mark band 2	Mark band 3
Carries out fitness tests which produce **basic** results, which are recorded with **limited** accuracy. Consideration of protocols and guidelines is **superficial**.	Carries out fitness tests which produce a **range** of results, which are recorded with **some** accuracy. **Some** consideration of protocols and guidelines is evident.	Carries out fitness tests to produce an **extensive range** of results, which are recorded with **precision**. Consideration of protocols and guidelines is **clearly** evident.
Interpretation of the results is **limited**.	Interpretation of the results is **clear** with **some** reference to normative data, reliability and validity.	Interpretation of the results is **clear** and **detailed** reference to normative data, reliability and validity is made.

L04 Be able to develop fitness training programmes

Design a fitness training programme

Fitness tests allow participants to work out their fitness strengths and weaknesses. Having carried out a range of fitness tests using the correct protocol, participants then need to commence a suitable training programme in order to work on the fitness components they feel they need to improve. However, there are a variety of considerations that need to be carefully evaluated when designing this programme. These include:

- What are the participant's fitness weaknesses?
- What is the participant's medical history?
- Does the participant have any current injuries?
- What are the aims of the training programme?
- What type of training should be used?
- What goals does the participant hope to achieve?
- How long should the training programme last?
- What equipment (if any) is required?
- How can the participant reflect on how training is going/has gone?
- When should the participant retest their fitness to see if improvement has occurred?

Gathering details about the person doing the training

It is important to work out whether a participant is fit enough and able to carry out a training programme. It is therefore advisable to take some simple information first, such as:

- name
- age
- gender
- weight
- recent or current injuries
- how accessible facilities are.

Having recorded these basic details, it is then advisable to carry out a more detailed questionnaire. A **questionnaire** is simply a series of questions to be answered truthfully.

PAR-Q

PAR-Q stands for 'physical activity readiness questionnaire', and it is a suitable starting point in determining whether the participant can increase the amount of physical activity in their life. It involves simple 'yes/no' questions and aims to identify whether the participant falls into the small number of people for whom physical activity might be unsuitable, generally on the grounds of medical advice.

Although participants can complete the questionnaire on their own, they may be guided by a coach or friend so that it can then be fully evaluated as to whether physical activity may be unadvisable.

Getting started

In small groups, discuss how easy it is to incorporate a training programme into your lives. Are facilities available? Do you have a suitable amount of free time? Do you need advice on how to do the programme? Whom could you get that from? Would you need to access some equipment? Where could you get that equipment from?

Links to other units

You will find the information in R041 to be very important when developing training programmes.

Key terms

Questionnaire A series of questions to be answered truthfully.

PAR-Q Physical activity readiness questionnaire – an introductory 'yes/no' questionnaire that aims to identify the small number of people for whom physical activity might be unsuitable on the grounds of medical advice.

Physical Activity Readiness Questionnaire (PAR-Q)

Many health benefits are associated with regular exercise. The completion of PAR-Q is a sensible first step if you are planning to increase the amount of physical activity in your life.

PAR-Q is designed to identify the small number of people for whom physical activity might not be appropriate or those who should seek medical advice before beginning a new activity.

Common sense is the best guide to answering these questions. Please read them carefully and circle your responses.

1. Has your doctor ever said that you have bone or joint problems (for example arthritis) that have been aggravated by exercise or might be made worse with exercise?	Y	N
2. Do you have high blood pressure?	Y	N
3. Do you have low blood pressure?	Y	N
4. Do you have diabetes or any other metabolic disease?	Y	N
5. Has your doctor ever said that you have a raised cholesterol level (above 6.2 mmol/L)?	Y	N
6. Has your doctor ever said that you have a heart condition and that you should only do physical activity recommended by a doctor?	Y	N
7. Have you ever felt pain in your chest when you do physical exercise?	Y	N
8. Is your doctor prescribing you drugs or medication?	Y	N
9. Have you ever suffered from unusual shortness of breath at rest or with mild exertion?	Y	N
10. Is there any history of coronary heart disease in your family?	Y	N
11. Do you often feel faint, have spells of severe dizziness or lose consciousness?	Y	N
12. Do you currently drink more than the average amount of alcohol per week (21 units for men, 14 units for women)?	Y	N
13. Do you currently smoke?	Y	N
14. Do you currently exercise less than three times a week?	Y	N
15. Are you, or is there any possibility that you might be, pregnant?	Y	N
16. Do you know of any other reason why you should not participate in a programme of physical activity?	Y	N

Figure 2.37 A PAR-Q questionnaire

Clarify the aims of the training programme

It is important that the coach/trainer sits down with the participant before training commences, to establish what training goals are to be achieved. Obviously, the scores achieved in fitness tests and the results of any pre-training assessments will affect this. It is common to carry out a **client progress review**, which is an interview used to set goals and re-evaluate if any changes need to be made. These reviews are carried out regularly during and after training. The main aims of this process are to outline:

- which components of fitness need to be prioritised
- how much the participant would like to improve.

Set realistic goals that can be measured

Many people use the acronym SMART as a guideline on how to set goals:

- **S**pecific – goals should not be vague (e.g. 'get fit') but instead should be focused (e.g. 'run 5K')

Group activity

In pairs, take turns to go through the PAR-Q questionnaire with your partner. Try to interpret the results. Is your partner fit and able to take part in physical activity?

Read about it

Read about PAR-Q:

www.verywellfit.com/ physical- activity-readiness-questionnaire-3120277

Key term

Client progress review
An interview used to set goals and re-evaluate if any changes need to be made.

- **M**easurable – goals should be able to be measured and assessed, e.g. run 5K in 25 minutes.
- **A**chievable – the performer should have the ability to achieve the goal.
- **R**ealistic - it should be possible for the participant to actually achieve the goal, e.g. if training for 5k in 25 minutes would require 6 sessions a week, this might not be realistic for a parent of young children
- **T**ime bound – goals should be set over a realistic period of time.

SMART goals are also mentioned on page 146 in Unit R044: Sport psychology, in relation to providing suitable motivation for participants.

Consider the following example of a 15-year-old who recently ran a 5K race in one hour and scored level 6 shuttle 5 in the multistage fitness test (classified as poor). Unrealistic goals might include:

- improve bleep test score to above level 10 within six weeks
- improve 5K run time by 20 minutes within 12 weeks.

More realistic, measurable goals might include:

- improvement of cardiovascular endurance
- improve bleep test score to above level 7 within six weeks
- improve 5K run time by five minutes within 12 weeks.

Further examples of realistic and measurable goals are given in Table 2.16.

Table 2.16 Examples of realistic and measurable goals

Current situation	Realistic and measurable goal to be achieved
20 years old Conducted a range of fitness tests: ● bleep test (below average) ● Illinois agility run test (average) ● vertical jump test (below average) ● sit-and-reach test (below average)	Desire to improve all-round fitness Aim to show an improved score (any improvement) in all tests within six weeks
17 years old Poor score in press-up test (score of 17)	Intent to improve strength Goal to record 20 or more press-ups for the test within one month

Duration of the training programme

When designing a training programme, it is important to accept that training gains can take time and therefore do not happen overnight. The coach or trainer should ensure that the participant has a suitable length of time in which to achieve their goals. Goals are often divided into short-, medium- and long-term goals. However, as a guide:

- initial goals are often set to be completed over six weeks
- these six-week goals can then be re-evaluated and lead into longer-term goals.

Figure 2.38 A fitness trainer agreeing goals to be achieved with their client

Suitability of activities

When designing a training programme, it is important to ensure that the activities and exercises used match the needs of the participant and the fitness target areas. This is the only way that training will actually improve what is being targeted. Some examples are shown in Table 2.17 as a guide.

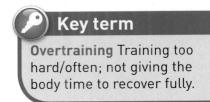

Key term

Overtraining Training too hard/often; not giving the body time to recover fully.

Table 2.17 Examples of suitable training activities for different target areas

Target area	Suitable activity
Cardiovascular endurance	Any aerobic activity, e.g. cycling, swimming, jogging, walking, rowing 20 minutes or more at 60–80% of maximum heart rate, e.g. treadmill run
Muscular endurance/ strength endurance	Repeated low-intensity contractions, e.g. press-ups, sit-ups, burpees, jumping over bar Weight training – low weight, high reps
Agility	Shuttles or circuits that involve speed work while changing direction, e.g. sprinting round cones
Speed	Speed ladders Interval sprints
Strength	Resistance training Weight training – heavy weight, low reps
Power	Interval training – high-intensity, short sharp activities Acceleration sprint training Plyometric training, e.g. box jumping, hurdle jumps
Improvement in general fitness	A mixture of all of the above Participant will generally include some low-intensity, long-duration aerobic training and some higher-intensity work

Organisation of activities

It is important that training sessions are suitably organised to take account of variance and rest.

Variance
This means ensuring that there are a variety of training methods, with the intention that training does not get boring.

Rest
It is important that rest days are included to prevent **overtraining** from occurring, which can result in extreme fatigue, injuries and hormonal imbalance. Rest allows the body to recuperate and to repair any minor muscle tears and remove waste products.

One day's rest may not be enough in a weekly programme, so it is common practice for those playing sport at weekends to take one day off training between Monday and Friday and a day off after performing at the weekend.

As well as planning for appropriate rest between sessions, participants should also have appropriate rest between sets or exercises. One way to express this is called a **work-to-rest ratio**. For example, a work-to-rest ratio of 2 : 1 means that they will work for twice as long as they rest.

Figure 2.39 A mix of lifting weights, moving objects and using kettle bells will provide some variation in a strength training programme

Table 2.18 Example guidelines for rest

Exercise schedule	Suggested rest
Strength training: heavy weights, approximately 1–6 reps, 2–6 sets	Rest for 2–5 minutes between sets
Muscular endurance training: low weights, approximately 6–12 reps, 3–6 sets	Rest for 30–90 seconds between sets
Interval training within a circuit for cardiovascular endurance Work for five minutes at a low intensity	Rest for five minutes before starting another five-minute exercise Work-to-rest ratio of 1:1
Circuit training for anaerobic gains, e.g. strength, power, speed, agility for beginners Work for 30–45 seconds at each circuit	Rest for 60–90 seconds between stations Work-to-rest ratio of 1:2
Circuit training for anaerobic gains, e.g. strength, power, speed, agility for beginners Work for 20 seconds at each circuit at maximal intensity	Rest for 10 seconds between stations Work-to-rest ratio of 2:1

Adaptability

It is important that the participant shows some **adaptability**. This means that they should show flexibility to adapt their programme if, for any reason, the session being performed cannot be followed precisely. Examples might include:

- having access to an indoor area or treadmill when running cannot be completed outside due to inclement weather
- using free weights if a resistance machine is broken.

Progression

It is important that the training programme allows the principle of progression to be applied (see page 36). This will mean that the programme needs to be evaluated regularly and adjusted as necessary. For example, if the programme is becoming too easy it might be important to look at:

- frequency – how often the person trains could be increased
- intensity – how hard/intense the training is could be increased
- time – how long each training session lasts could be increased
- type – the type of training could be changed
- adherence – how strictly you stick to the training plan should be maintained.

Evaluate the effectiveness of the training programme

It is important to evaluate how successful a training programme has been. This will involve several stages and questions being answered.

Measurement and reflection

1 First and foremost, it is important to re-do the fitness tests that were undertaken prior to starting training. This will give an objective measure of whether improvement has taken place. Results from the fitness tests can be compared to the original results.

Key terms

Work-to-rest ratio The amount of exercise (work) compared to the amount of rest.

Adaptability Flexibility to adapt a programme if, for any reason, the session being performed cannot be followed precisely.

2   Conduct another aspect of the client progress review (see page 73) to evaluate how well training has gone.

Figure 2.40 Evaluating client progress

Improvement

Having finished the initial stages of training, the participant needs to decide how improvement could continue and what changes to make to the training programme in the future. Some examples of this are shown below:

- **Results** – were the results of the programme acceptable? If not, why not? For example, should training continue for a longer period of time to allow progression to occur to a greater extent?
- **Boredom/variety** – was any aspect of the programme boring or tedious? Should the participant look to increase variety in the programme or change what they are doing, for example changing their running route, using some indoor treadmill work and some outdoor running work, or incorporating some cycling or swimming within a running programme?
- **Intensity** – was the programme too easy, causing progression to be limited or slow? Does the intensity need to be adjusted so that fitness improvements are accelerated?

> **Links to other units**
>
> You can find further information on this topic in Units R043, R044, R045 and R046.

Know it!

1   State three components of fitness and suggest appropriate exercises or activities to develop these components.

2   What is meant by the term 'variance'?

3   Suggest five questions that could be asked during a 'client progress review'.

4   Give an example of how intensity may be changed within a programme after evaluating how it is proceeding.

Stretch activity

1 Suggest how variance could be applied to a weight training programme and to a continuous training programme.

2 Suggest reasons why fitness training programmes may not work. What can be done to address these issues so that the programme is a success in the future?

Read about it

Planning for appropriate rest:

www.coachkaehler.com/new/content-recovery

Planning an appropriate circuit:

https://www.acefitness.org/education-and-resources/
professional/expert-articles/5050/how-to-create-an-effective-circuit-workout

Evaluating the success of a fitness training programme:

https://gmb.io/fitness-programming

Assessment preparation

Think about the tasks that your teacher may set you to assess your knowledge of fitness training programmes. Make sure that you know:

● how to design a fitness training programme

● how to evaluate a fitness training programme.

How will you demonstrate that you have interpreted results appropriately and thought about how training could be suitably amended in the future?

Mark scheme

LO4: Be able to develop fitness training programmes		
Mark band 1	Mark band 2	Mark band 3
The programme aims show **some relevance** to **some** of the initial data gathered. There has been **limited** application of principles of training in its design. The programme meets **few** of the specific needs and requirements identified in the aims.	The programme aims show **relevance** to **most** of the initial data gathered. **Most** of the principles of training have been applied with **some effectiveness** in its design. The programme meets **most** of the specific needs and requirements identified in the aims.	The programme aims show **relevance** to **all** of the initial data gathered. **All** of the principles of training have been applied **effectively** in its design. The programme meets **all** of the specific needs and requirements identified in the aims.
Needs **some** individual support to design the fitness training programme.	May need **minimal** individual support to design the fitness training programme.	Fitness training programme is designed **independently**.
Mark band 1	Mark band 2	Mark band 3
Evaluation is **brief** with **limited** reflection on the design and delivery of the programme; suggestions for improvement are general rather than specific.	Evaluation is **detailed** and reflects on **many** aspects of the design and delivery of the programme. Ideas for improvement are **mostly relevant** and **considered**.	Evaluation is **comprehensive** and reflects on **most** aspects of the design and delivery of the programme. Ideas for improvement are **specific** and **justified**.

R043 The body's response to physical activity

About this unit

Physical activity is known to be essential in maintaining good health. Many careers within the sport, leisure and health industries require their employees to understand how the body is affected by short-term and long-term exercise. This type of knowledge enables the individual to improve specific body systems to optimise sports performance and promote healthier lifestyles.

Completion of this unit will help you understand key aspects of the musculo-skeletal and cardio-respiratory systems, and to investigate some of the changes that occur during short- and long-term exercise.

Learning outcomes

L01 Know the key components of the musculo-skeletal and cardio-respiratory systems, their functions and roles

L02 Understand the importance of the musculo-skeletal and cardio-respiratory systems in health and fitness

L03 Be able to assess the short-term effects of physical activity on the musculo-skeletal and cardio-respiratory systems

L04 Be able to assess the long-term effects of physical activity on the musculo-skeletal and cardio-respiratory systems

How will I be assessed?

This unit is internally assessed through a written assignment set and marked by your centre. It is worth 25 per cent of the overall mark for the OCR Level 1/2 Cambridge National Certificate in Sport Science. It is estimated that the assignment will take about ten hours to complete and it is worth 60 marks.

OCR provides a model assignment for this unit: http://ocr.org.uk/qualifications/cambridge-nationals/cambridge-nationals-sport-science-level-1-2-j802-j812/assessment

For LO1

You need to have knowledge and understanding of:

- key components of the musculo-skeletal system and its function
- key components of the cardio-respiratory system and its function
- the role of the musculo-skeletal system in producing movement
- the role of the cardio-respiratory system during physical activity.

For LO2

You need to have knowledge and understanding of:

- benefits of cardio-respiratory fitness in everyday life

- benefits of muscular strength and flexibility
- benefits of muscular endurance.

For LO3

You need to have knowledge and understanding of:

- different short-term effects of physical activity on the musculo-skeletal and cardio-respiratory systems, and reasons for these
- ways to measure and record the short-term effects of physical activity on the musculo-skeletal and cardio-respiratory systems.

For LO4

You need to have knowledge and understanding of:

- long-term effects of physical activity on the musculo-skeletal and cardio-respiratory systems, and reasons for these
- ways to measure and record the long-term effects of physical activity on the musculo-skeletal and cardio-respiratory systems.

LO1 Know the key components of the musculo-skeletal and cardio-respiratory systems, their functions and roles

Key components of the musculo-skeletal system and its function

The musculo-skeletal system is made up of bones, muscles, joints and **connective tissue**. These structures work together to provide movement.

Major bones

The human skeleton consists of over a hundred major bones that provide our bodies with general shape, such as height and build, and provide attachments for muscles so that we can move.

The skeleton may be divided into the bones that form the central skeleton and those that form the limbs (arms and legs).

The central skeleton contains the bones of the head, the **cranium**, and the bones in the chest. The cranium surrounds and protects the brain. The bones in the chest include the **ribs**, the **sternum** (sometimes called the breast bone) and the **vertebrae** (sometimes called the backbone).

The ribs partially enclose and protect the chest cavity, where many vital organs including the heart and the lungs are located. The sternum is a flat bone at the front and centre of the chest. The ribs and sternum make up the 'ribcage'. The backbone is made up of 33 individual vertebrae that allow for movement while, at the same time, surrounding and protecting the spinal cord.

Key terms

Connective tissue White tissue providing support.

Cranium Skull bone surrounding and protecting the brain.

Ribs Bones surrounding the heart and lungs, forming the chest cavity.

Sternum The breast bone.

Vertebrae Many single bones joined together to form the backbone.

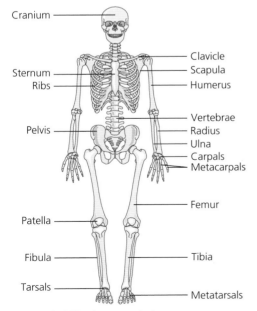

Figure 3.1 The human skeleton

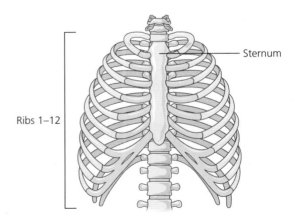

Figure 3.2 Bones in the chest

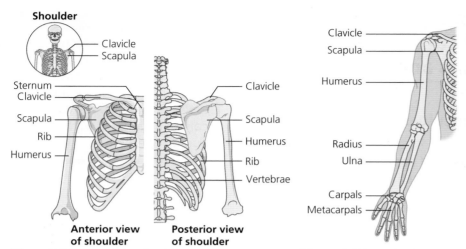

Figure 3.3 Bones of the shoulder

Figure 3.4 Bones in the arm

Key terms

Clavicle The collar bone.

Scapula The shoulder blade.

Humerus Bone in the upper arm.

Radius Bone of the forearm; attaches to the thumb side of the wrist.

Ulna Bone of the forearm; forms the point of the elbow.

Carpals Bones in the wrist.

Metacarpals Bones in the palm of the hand.

Pelvic girdle Also called the pelvis; attached to the backbone; forms the hip joint with the femur.

Tibia The shin bone; forms the knee joint with the femur.

Fibula Bone in the lower leg that forms the ankle.

Patella The knee cap; covers the knee joint.

Tarsals Bones in the foot that form the ankle joint.

Metatarsals Bones in the foot.

The arms are attached to the central skeleton by the **clavicle** (sometimes called the collar bone) and the **scapula** (sometimes called the shoulder blade). The clavicle is a long bone that connects the scapula to the sternum. The scapula is a triangular flat bone that lies on the back of the chest cavity. It connects the clavicle to the humerus in the arm.

The bones of the arm include the **humerus** in the upper arm, the **radius** and **ulna** in the forearm and the **carpals** in the wrist. The bones in the hand are the **metacarpals**.

The humerus forms two joints: the shoulder joint with the scapula, and the elbow joint with the radius and the ulna. The radius and ulna form the wrist joint with the carpals.

The legs are attached to the central skeleton by the **pelvic girdle**. The bone in the thigh is called the femur. The pelvic girdle is attached to the lower part of the backbone and also forms the hip joint with the femur.

The bones in the lower leg include the **tibia** (sometimes called the shin bone), the **fibula** and the **patella** (sometimes called the knee cap). The bones of the foot are the **tarsals** and **metatarsals**.

The tibia forms the knee joint with the femur. The patella protects the knee joint from trauma. The tibia and fibula attach to the tarsals forming the ankle joint.

 Group activity

Go back to your getting started diagram. Add any bones that you did not include initially and check that you have used the correct terminology.

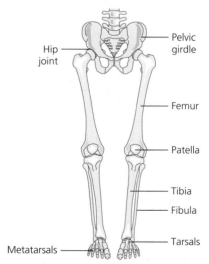

Figure 3.5 Bones in the leg

Skeletal muscle groups

Bones move because groups of **skeletal muscles** pull them. The main skeletal muscles forming the upper body are the deltoids, trapezius, latissimus dorsi, pectorals, biceps, triceps and abdominals.

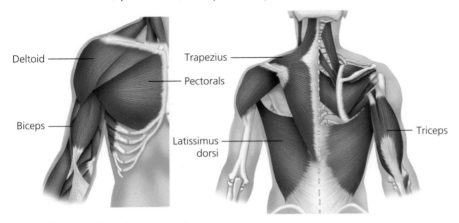

Figure 3.6 Muscles of the upper body

The **deltoids** are the muscles that 'cap' the shoulder and move the upper arm. The **trapezius** is found in the upper back and moves the scapula and the head. The **latissimus dorsi** are large muscles in the back that attach to the upper arms and cause a variety of shoulder movements. The **pectorals** are the large muscles of the chest which cause movements of the upper arm.

The **biceps** are the muscles at the front of the arm that cause bending at the elbow joint. The **triceps** are located at the back of the upper arm and cause straightening at the elbow joint.

The **abdominals** are sometimes referred to as the 'six pack'. The abdominal muscles protect and hold internal organs in place and help with posture.

 Group activity

In pairs, select a sport you are familiar with that uses frequent arm movements, for example badminton or tennis, and discuss which muscles are being used.

The main skeletal muscles of the lower body are the gluteals, hamstrings, quadriceps, gastrocnemius and soleus.

Stretch activity

Create a table that lists the bones you have covered so far. In the second column, add detailed information about the functions that these bones perform.

 Group activity

Working in pairs, write the names of any muscles you know on sticky notes (one muscle per note). Place the notes on your body where you think those muscles are.

Key terms

Deltoids Muscles on the shoulder joint that move the upper arm.

Trapezius Muscle at the top of the back that moves the scapula and head.

Latissimus dorsi Muscle at the side of the back that moves the upper arm.

Pectorals Muscles in the chest that move the upper arm.

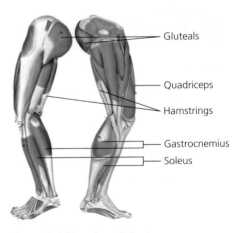

Figure 3.7 Muscles of the legs

The **gluteals** are the muscles of the buttocks, which are used during running. The **hamstrings** are the muscles at the back of the upper leg that bend the knee. The **quadriceps** are the muscles at the front of the leg that straighten the leg. The **gastrocnemius and soleus** are the muscles in the calves that help to point the toes.

 Group activity

Complete ten squats. Explain to a partner which muscles are being used and where they are located.

Stretch activity

Discuss the function that the muscles used in the group activity are performing.

Read about it

Muscular system:

www.innerbody.com/image/musfov.html

www.getbodysmart.com/muscular-system

Synovial joints

A **synovial joint** joins bones together with a cavity that encloses the ends of the bones. The cavity is filled with fluid that allows the joints to move freely. There are six types of synovial joint in our skeletons.

A **pivot joint**, for example the joint between the first and second vertebrae of the neck, is where the rounded end of one bone fits into a ring formed by the other bone. This allows rotational or turning movements, for example rotation of the head.

The wrist is a **condyloid joint**, where the curved surface of the carpal bones joins with the radius of the forearm. The joint allows the wrist to move from side to side as well as forwards and backwards.

Stretch activity

Referring to the group activity at the bottom of page 83, add detail about the functions that those muscles are performing.

 Key terms

Gluteals Buttock muscles, which are used when running.

Hamstrings Muscles at the back of the upper leg that bend the knee.

Gastrocnemius and soleus The calf muscles used to push the foot off the ground when running.

Synovial joint A freely moveable joint.

Pivot joint Where the round end on one bone fits into a ring formed by another bone, for example the vertebrae of the neck which allow head rotation.

Condyloid joint Where the curved end of one bone fits against another curved end, for example at the wrist.

Figure 3.8 A pivot joint

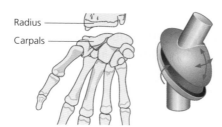

Radius

Carpals

Figure 3.9 A condyloid joint

 Group activity

Stand up – you have 30 seconds to point to as many parts of the body that have joints as you can. Start at the top of your head and work down. How many did you point to?

The thumb forms a **saddle joint**, where one of the bones forming the joint is shaped like a saddle with the other bone resting on it like a rider on a horse. This type of joint allows your thumb to move towards your fingers.

A **gliding joint** allows some limited side to side and back and forth movements between the almost flat surfaces of the bones in the joint. The joint between the carpals in the wrist is a gliding joint.

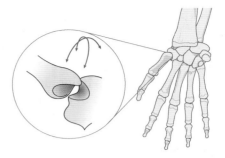

Figure 3.10 A saddle joint

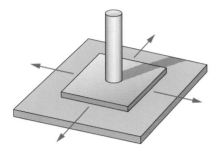

Figure 3.11 A gliding joint

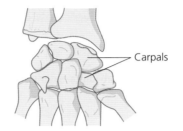

Carpals

A **ball and socket joint** has a rounded surface of one bone moving within a depression on another bone. The hip and shoulder are both examples of ball and socket joints.

A **hinge joint** is where the bones in the joint are shaped so that movement is only possible in one direction: forwards and back. The knee and elbow are both examples of hinge joints.

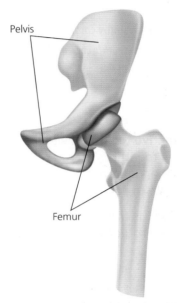

Pelvis

Femur

Figure 3.12 The hip: a ball and socket joint

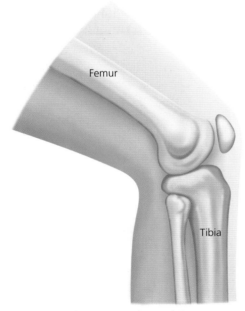

Femur

Tibia

Figure 3.13 The knee: a hinge joint

Key terms

Saddle joint Where a saddle-shaped bone fits on another, for example in the thumb.

Gliding joint Where one bone can slide over another, for example the carpals in the wrist.

Ball and socket joint Where the ball-shaped end of one bone fits into the socket of another, for example the hip.

Hinge joint Where the end of one bone fits against another bone allowing movement in only one direction, for example the knee.

Group activity

Watch this video of a weightlifter performing a dead lift:
www.youtube.com/watch?v=op9kVnSso6Q

Locate the joints being used to perform the movement and identify the types of joints they are.

Stretch activity

Discuss the functions of the joints used during the dead lift activity.

Read about it

Synovial joints:

www.mananatomy.com/basic-anatomy/synovial-joints

https://study.com/academy/lesson/the-six-types-of-synovial-joints-examples-definition.html

Connective tissue

Connective tissue provides support and holds the body's other tissues together. There are three main types of connective tissue: cartilage, ligaments and tendons. All three are made up of fibres and are white in colour because they have a very limited blood supply.

Cartilage is a flexible tissue found at the ends of bones where it forms a protective covering. Your ears are also made up of cartilage.

Key term

Cartilage Flexible tissue; forms padding at the ends of long bones; forms ears.

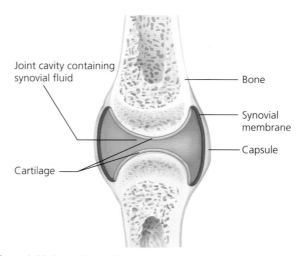

Figure 3.14 Synovial joint with cartilage

Ligaments are fibrous bands that help to stabilise the bones in synovial joints by connecting bone to bone.

Tendons attach muscles to bone. When a muscle contracts, it pulls on its tendon, which in turn pulls on a bone to cause movement.

Group activity

There are three types of connective tissue. In small groups, explain where you might find them in the body and what the function of each of them is.

Stretch activity

Create a detailed diagram or report locating and identifying the main skeletal muscles and joints.

Read about it

Structure and function of connective tissue:

https://sciencing.com/7-types-connective-tissue-8768445.html

Functions of the musculo-skeletal system

The functions of the skeleton include:

- **Support** – bones are solid and rigid; they keep us upright and hold the rest of the body (muscles and organs) in place.
- **Movement** – the skeleton helps the body to move by providing anchor points for the muscles to pull against so, when muscles contract, we move.
- **Protection** of vital organs – certain parts of the skeleton surround the body's organs and protect them from external forces; for example, the brain is protected by the cranium, and the ribs protect the heart and lungs. This function is especially important in activities that involve contact, such as rugby or boxing.
- **Blood cell production** – the inner marrow of bones such as the sternum and ribs produce red and white blood cells. Red blood cells are important for physical activity because they carry oxygen to the working muscles. White blood cells are important to fight off infections in order to keep us healthy.

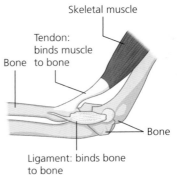

Skeletal muscle

Tendon: binds muscle to bone

Bone

Bone

Ligament: binds bone to bone

Figure 3.15 Tendons and ligaments

Key components of the cardio-respiratory system and its function

The cardio-respiratory system is made up of the heart, respiratory system, blood vessels and blood. These structures work together to provide oxygen and nutrients for our body, remove waste products from our body, and regulate our body temperature.

Read about it

The cardio-respiratory system:

www.shoppingtrolley.net/cardio-respiratory-system.shtml

www.pelinks4u.org/articles/TA1Health1009.pdf

Heart

The heart is a muscular organ (about the size of a closed fist) found in the chest that pumps blood around the body. It is divided into separate left and right sides, and each side has an upper and lower chamber. The upper chambers are the **atria**, which collect blood from veins; the lower chambers are the **ventricles**, which pump out blood through the arteries. One-way **valves** are present in the heart to stop blood flowing in the wrong direction.

The right side of the heart takes in deoxygenated blood through the veins and delivers it to the lungs for oxygenation. The oxygenated blood returns from the lungs to the left side of the heart and is then pumped into various arteries that provide oxygen and nutrients to the body tissues by transporting the blood throughout the body.

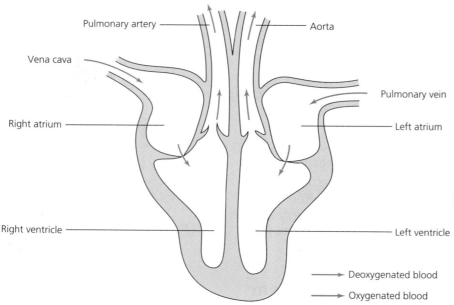

Figure 3.16 Structure of the heart

 Group activity

Draw a basic diagram of the heart and identify the key components.

 Key terms

Atria Upper chambers of the heart that collect blood from veins.

Ventricles Lower chambers of the heart that pump out blood through the arteries.

Valves Prevent the backflow of blood in the heart.

Trachea Tube connecting the mouth and nose to the lungs.

 Group activity

In groups of three you should each select a key component of the heart (as identified in the group activity above) and explain its function.

Respiratory system

The respiratory system involves the parts of the body that are concerned with breathing. When we breathe in, air moves through the mouth and nose and travels into the **trachea** (windpipe). The trachea carries air, which contains oxygen, to the lungs. Near the lungs, the trachea divides into two tubes called bronchi, one to each lung. Once inside the lung, the bronchi split several ways, forming smaller and smaller bronchi. The small bronchi further divide into bronchioles, which are narrow tubes less than 1 mm in diameter.

At the end of each bronchiole are the **alveoli**. Several alveoli usually come from one bronchiole, forming a little clump that resembles a cluster of grapes. The surface of the alveoli allows oxygen from air breathed in to pass into the blood and carbon dioxide to be removed from the blood and breathed out.

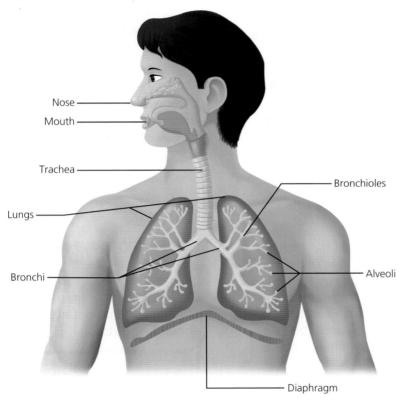

Nose
Mouth
Trachea
Lungs
Bronchi
Bronchioles
Alveoli
Diaphragm

Figure 3.17 The respiratory system

When we breathe in, the dome-shaped **diaphragm** muscle, which separates the chest from the abdomen, contracts and flattens. This draws air into the lungs. To breathe out, the diaphragm relaxes back to its normal shape and air is forced out of the lungs.

Group activity

Working in pairs, explain what happens to the diaphragm when you breathe in and out.

Blood

Blood is a specialised body fluid. It has four main components: **plasma**, **red blood cells**, **white blood cells** and **platelets**. Blood has many different functions, including:

- transporting oxygen and nutrients to the tissues
- protecting the body by forming blood clots to prevent excess blood loss and carrying cells that fight infection

Key terms

Alveoli Tiny air sacs in the lungs.

Diaphragm Main muscle of respiration that draws air into the lungs when it contracts and helps force air out of the lungs when it relaxes.

Plasma Fluid part of the blood that transports blood cells and dissolved nutrients.

Red blood cells Component of blood involved in transporting oxygen and carbon dioxide.

White blood cells Component of blood involved in fighting infection.

Platelets Component of blood involved in blood clotting.

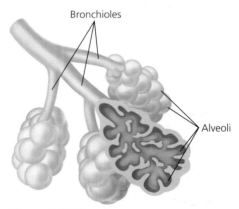

Bronchioles
Alveoli

Figure 3.18 Alveoli

Group activity

On a large piece of paper (A3 or flipchart paper) sketch an outline of a body. Use it to identify the key components of the respiratory system.

- transporting waste products, such as carbon dioxide to the lungs
- transporting blood to the kidneys and liver, which filter and clean the blood
- regulating body temperature.

The liquid part of blood is called plasma. The main job of plasma is to transport blood cells throughout the body along with nutrients and other chemicals.

Red blood cells contain a protein called haemoglobin that carries oxygen from the lungs to the rest of the body and then returns carbon dioxide from the body to the lungs, so it can be breathed out.

White blood cells protect the body from infection.

Platelets help the blood clotting process.

Blood vessels

There are three types of blood vessel in the body:

- **Arteries** mainly carry oxygenated blood away from the heart. Arteries are elastic but have thick muscular walls to maintain high blood pressure. The main arteries in the body include the **aorta**, which carries oxygenated blood away from the heart to the body's tissues; the **pulmonary artery**, which carries deoxygenated blood away from the heart and towards the lungs; and the **carotid artery**, which carries oxygenated blood to the head.
- **Veins** mainly carry deoxygenated blood back to the heart. They have valves to ensure that the blood flows in one direction. Blood flows from the capillaries into very small veins, then into larger veins that lead back to the heart.
- **Capillaries** are tiny, thin-walled blood vessels that join arteries (which carry blood away from the heart) and veins (which carry blood back to the heart). The thin walls of the capillaries allow gaseous exchange at the lungs, where oxygen passes from the alveoli into the blood, and carbon dioxide passes from the blood into the alveoli. Nutrients also diffuse from the blood in the capillaries into the surrounding tissues, and waste products diffuse from the tissues into the blood.

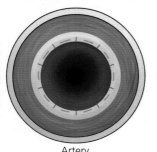 

Artery   Vein   Capillary

Figure 3.19 Blood vessels

Key terms

Arteries Thick muscular blood vessels that carry blood away from the heart.

Veins Thin-walled blood vessels that return blood to the heart; they have one-way valves.

Capillaries Tiny, thin blood vessels that join arteries and veins; the site of gaseous exchange.

Group activity

Create a mind map showing the four main components of blood, adding details about their functions.

Group activity

Write down reasons why we need blood vessels.

Stretch activity

There are three types of blood vessel in the body. Identify these and explain the different functions of each.

Functions of the cardio-respiratory system

The functions of the cardio-respiratory system include:

- taking air into the lungs and then taking oxygen from the lungs into the blood
- moving oxygenated blood from the lungs into the body, while at the same time moving deoxygenated blood from the body back to the lungs via the heart
- distributing nutrients to cells around the body
- removing waste products, such as carbon dioxide, from muscles and other organs
- regulating body temperature by absorbing and redistributing heat through blood flow to the skin
- transporting hormones, enzymes and other chemicals around the body
- preventing dehydration by keeping fluid volume constant.

Read about it

Functions of the cardiovascular system:

www.ptdirect.com/training-design/anatomy-and-physiology/major-functions-of-the-cardiovascular-system-2013-a-closer-look

Role of the musculo-skeletal system in producing movement

The many muscles, bones, joints and connective tissues in your body work together as the musculo-skeletal system to produce movement.

Types of movement

Scientists use technical terms for the different types of movement that your body can do:

- **Flexion** refers to movement where the angle between two bones decreases. It is commonly known as bending. When you perform a biceps curl, by bending your arm at the elbow, the movement is flexion.
- **Extension** refers to movement where the angle between two bones increases. It is otherwise known as straightening. When you straighten your arm at the elbow following the flexion of a biceps curl, the movement is extension.
- **Abduction** is the movement of part of the body away from the midline of the body. When you raise your legs to the side during a star jump in gymnastics, this is abduction.

 Group activity

Create a newspaper article that details the functions of the cardio-respiratory system to an audience of teenagers. You may want it to have more than one page.

 Key terms

Flexion Movement where the angle between bones decreases (bending).

Extension Movement where the angle between bones increases (straightening).

Abduction Moving a limb away from the midline of the body.

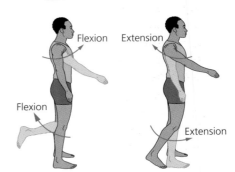

Figure 3.20 Flexion and extension

 Group activity

Perform two biceps curl activities (you do not need any weights). Which part of the movement is flexion and which part is extension?

Stretch activity

Draw a stick diagram showing the musculo-skeletal movement during a biceps curl. Label where the bones flex and extend.

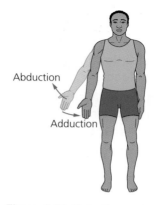

- **Adduction** is the movement of part of the body towards the midline of the body. When you bring your legs together from an astride position of a star jump, this is adduction.

 Group activity

In pairs, one person instructs their partner on how to do a star jump; the partner should perform the actions as instructed.

Swap roles. This time the person instructs their partner to complete three star jumps, however you can only use the words 'abduction' and 'adduction'.

Figure 3.21 Abduction and adduction

- **Rotation** refers to a turning or twisting movement. When you turn your hips during a golf swing, this is rotation. A more obvious example would be when you turn your head to the side.

- **Circumduction** is a conical movement of a limb extending from the shoulder or hip. Arm circles during a dance routine involve circumduction.

 Key terms

Adduction Moving a limb towards the midline of the body.

Rotation Turning part of the body around its axis.

Circumduction Conical movement of an extended limb.

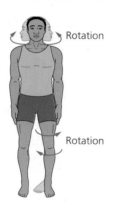

Figure 3.22 Rotation

Figure 3.23 Circumduction

Read about it

Movement at joints:

www.teachpe.com/gcse_anatomy/joints.php

Functions of connective tissue

The main function of connective tissue is to support other tissues, especially during movement.

- **Cartilage** forms a protective covering over the ends of bones. It absorbs the shocks of movement and provides a smooth surface to reduce friction during movement.

- **Ligaments** help to stabilise the bones in synovial joints by connecting bone to bone. They limit movement in certain directions in some joints but allow movement in other directions.
- **Tendons** attach muscles to bone. When a muscle contracts it pulls on its tendon, which in turn pulls on a bone to cause movement.

Muscle contractions

There are two types of muscle contraction: isometric and isotonic.

During **isometric contractions**, the muscle stays the same length. For example, while performing a handstand, many of the body's muscles are contracting, but there is no movement as the balance is being held.

Isotonic contractions occur when the muscle contracts and changes length. This causes movement of a body part. There are two types of isotonic contraction:

- **Concentric contractions** are those where the muscle shortens as it contracts. An example is bending the elbow from straight to fully flexed, caused by a concentric contraction of the biceps. Concentric contractions are the most common type of muscle contraction and occur frequently in sporting activities.
- **Eccentric contractions** occur when the muscle lengthens as it contracts. This is less common than concentric contractions and usually involves the control or slowing down of a movement.

  There are two distinct phases in a squat: first, when the legs are flexed (bent) at the knee, and then when the legs are extended (straightened) at the knee. In the extension phase of a squat, the quadriceps contract concentrically to allow the movement to occur. In the knee flexion phase of a squat, the quadriceps contract eccentrically to control the descent and lower the body slowly towards the ground.

Figure 3.24 Handstands involve isometric muscle contractions

Figure 3.25 During the upwards phase of a biceps curl, the biceps contract concentrically

Key terms

Isometric contractions
Where the muscle contracts but there is no movement.

Isotonic contractions
Where the muscle contracts and movement occurs.

Figure 3.26 During the downwards phase of a squat, the quadriceps contract eccentrically

Read about it

Types of muscle contraction:

www.teachpe.com/anatomy/types_of_muscle_contractions.php

www.netfit.co.uk/articles/fitness_articles/types_muscle_contractions.htm

Role of the cardio-respiratory system during physical activity

The heart, lungs and blood work together as parts of the cardio-respiratory system during physical activity to deliver oxygen and other nutrients to the working muscles and to remove carbon dioxide and other waste products.

Heart rate

During physical activity, your heart beats faster to pump blood to the working muscles. This blood contains the oxygen that the muscles need in order for them to contract.

Your **heart rate** – the number of heart beats per minute – can be taken at any point on the body where an artery is close to the surface and a pulse can be felt. The most common places to measure heart rate using this method are at the wrist (radial artery) and the neck (carotid artery):

- **Radial pulse** (wrist) – place your index and middle fingers together on the opposite wrist, about 2 cm below the fold of the wrist, in line with the index finger. Once you find a pulse, count the number of beats you feel within a one-minute period to measure your heart rate.
- **Carotid pulse** (neck) – to measure your heart rate at the neck, place your first two fingers into the groove on either side of the windpipe until you can feel the pulse. Be careful not to press too hard, then count the number of beats for a minute.

You can estimate the per-minute heart rate by counting over 15 seconds and multiplying this figure by four. A normal resting heart rate can range anywhere from 40 to 100 beats per minute. Your resting heart rate can vary with your fitness level and with age. The fitter you are, generally the lower your resting heart rate.

Read about it

How do I check my pulse?

www.nhs.uk/common-health-questions/accidents-first-aid-and-treatments/how-do-i-check-my-pulse

Classroom discussion

Discuss the effects of exercise on the body. Which effects occur first? Which effects take longer to occur?

Figure 3.27 Taking a carotid pulse

Group activity

Sit down and measure your heart rate using your:

1 radial pulse
2 carotid pulse.

Stretch activity

Explain what happens to your heart rate after you have completed ten star jumps.

Blood pressure

When the heart beats, it pumps blood into the arteries. **Cardiac output** is the volume of blood that the heart is able to pump out in one minute. It is usually measured in litres per minute.

Two major factors form the cardiac output: the heart rate, which is the number of times the heart beats each minute, and the **stroke volume,** which is the volume of blood that leaves the heart during each contraction.

Both an increase in heart rate and/or an increase in stroke volume will result in an increase in cardiac output.

The blood that leaves the heart (the cardiac output) is under pressure in the arteries so that it can reach all parts of the body.

Blood pressure is measured in millimetres of mercury (mmHg). There are two measurements:

- **systolic blood pressure** – the higher blood pressure measurement that occurs when the heart beats, pushing blood through the arteries
- **diastolic blood pressure** – the lower blood pressure measurement that occurs when the heart rests between beats.

Both systolic and diastolic blood pressures are measured and then given as two values. A young, fit person should have a blood pressure of about 120 over 70, which means their systolic pressure is 120 mmHg and their diastolic pressure is 70 mmHg.

Read about it

Blood pressure readings explained:

www.healthline.com/health/high-blood-pressure-hypertension/blood-pressure-reading-explained

Vascular shunt mechanism

Arteries carry mainly oxygenated blood away from the heart under high pressure.

Small arteries have rings of muscle in their walls that can narrow and widen the diameter of these arteries in order to decrease or increase blood flow to a particular part of the body. When the rings of muscle in the small arteries contract, it narrows those arteries and reduces the flow of blood through them. This is called **vasoconstriction**.

The small arteries can also widen – **vasodilation** – to allow more blood to flow through them to the tissues. Vasodilation occurs during exercise to allow more blood and, therefore, more oxygen to flow to the exercising muscles. Moving blood to those parts of the body that have a greater demand for it is called the **vascular shunt mechanism**. The vascular shunt mechanism will direct the flow of

Key terms

Cardiac output Amount of blood leaving the heart per minute.

Stroke volume Amount of blood leaving the heart with each beat.

Systolic blood pressure Blood pressure when the heart is contracting.

Diastolic blood pressure Blood pressure when the heart is relaxed.

Vascular shunt mechanism Mechanism that changes the size of arteries to move blood to where it is needed most.

blood to those muscles of the body involved in sport and physical activities, such as the legs during running. At the same time, less blood will be directed towards other parts of the body where demand for blood is not as great, for example inactive muscles and organs such as the kidneys and the stomach.

Read about it

Complete this exercise on the vascular shunt mechanism:
www.teachnetuk.org.uk/2007%20Projects/PE-Heart_Vascular/heart-vascular/Ex15-Vascular%20Shunt%20Cloze.htm

Breathing mechanism

The breathing mechanism involves a two-stage process. **Inhalation** is the intake of air into the lungs, which is brought about by increasing the volume of the chest cavity. **Exhalation** is the expulsion of air from the lungs by reducing the volume of the chest cavity.

Both inhalation and exhalation involve the use of muscles. The diaphragm is a sheet of muscle that separates the chest from the abdomen. The intercostal muscles are found between the ribs.

Contraction of the dome-shaped diaphragm causes it to flatten, thus enlarging the chest cavity. At the same time, contraction of the intercostal muscles causes the ribs to rise, also increasing the size of the chest cavity. When the chest cavity expands, its volume increases. This reduces the pressure in the chest cavity and air is sucked into the lungs.

During exhalation, the breathing muscles relax. The diaphragm returns to its dome shape, the weight of the ribs causes them to descend, and the chest volume decreases. The reduction in the size of the chest cavity forces air out of the lungs.

Group activity

List three different sports and identify which muscles will be using the vascular shunt mechanism.

Key terms

Inhalation Breathing in.
Exhalation Breathing out.

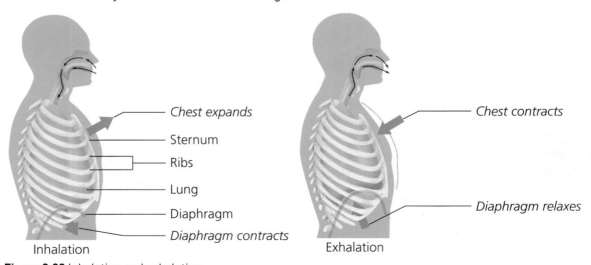

Inhalation — Chest expands / Sternum / Ribs / Lung / Diaphragm / *Diaphragm contracts*

Exhalation — *Chest contracts* / *Diaphragm relaxes*

Figure 3.28 Inhalation and exhalation

Read about it

Mechanism of breathing:

www.teachpe.com/anatomy/breathing.php

Internal respiration

The basic function of the lungs and alveoli is the exchange of gases, more usually called internal respiration. Capillaries carrying blood surround the alveoli. The movement of **oxygen** from the lungs into the blood, and the movement of **carbon dioxide** from the blood into the lungs, occur through the walls of the alveoli.

Internal respiration at the lungs takes place by diffusion. Oxygen and carbon dioxide move from a high concentration to a low concentration; this means that the oxygen in the alveoli, which is at a relatively high concentration, diffuses into the blood capillaries where the oxygen concentration is lower.

The same thing happens with carbon dioxide. Blood in the capillaries surrounding the alveoli contains a relatively high concentration of carbon dioxide and the alveoli contain a lower concentration. Thus, carbon dioxide diffuses into the alveoli from the blood and is eventually breathed out.

Aerobic and anaerobic respiration

When you exercise, you need to supply energy for muscle contractions. This is achieved in two different ways: through aerobic and anaerobic respiration.

Aerobic energy is usually supplied by breaking down glucose using oxygen. The aerobic energy system is used at low to moderate levels of exertion. Walking, jogging and resting are good examples of activities where the energy for muscle contractions is provided aerobically.

The process may be summarised as:

glucose + oxygen → energy + carbon dioxide + water

Figure 3.29 Jogging is an aerobic exercise

You can see from the equation that glucose is broken down using oxygen to provide energy, with water and carbon dioxide produced as waste products.

The **anaerobic** energy system is used for activities lasting less than a minute. Lactic acid is produced as a waste product. Sprinting, jumping and shot-putting are examples of activities where the energy is provided anaerobically.

In the anaerobic energy system, no oxygen is used. Because of this, the glucose is converted into lactic acid while producing the energy needed for the activity.

The process may be summarised as:

glucose → energy + lactic acid

The build-up of lactic acid in muscles causes fatigue and eventually pain, and the exercise has to slow down or, if strenuous, stop. Because of this, activities involving the anaerobic energy system cannot be continued for more than a minute or so.

Figure 3.30 Sprinting is an anaerobic exercise

Links to other units

You can find further information on this topic in Units R041, R042, R045 and R046.

Group activity

Create a list of ten sports and identify whether they are mainly aerobic or anaerobic.

Stretch activity

Create a Venn diagram showing sports that use aerobic, anaerobic or both energy systems.

Know it!

1   Name the bones found in the arm.
2   Name the bones found in the leg.
3   Name the muscles causing movement at the shoulder.
4   What type of synovial joints are found at the shoulder, knee and wrist?
5   Name three types of connective tissue.
6   Name the four functions of the musculo-skeletal system.
7   What are the key components of the cardio-respiratory system?
8   What are the key components of blood?
9   What are the main functions of the cardio-respiratory system?
10   Describe the following types of movement: flexion, adduction and circumduction.
11   Explain the difference between isometric and isotonic muscle contractions.
12   Explain the difference between aerobic and anaerobic respiration.

Read about it

Aerobic and anaerobic exercise:

www.bbc.com/bitesize/guides/zy2wmnb/revision/2

Prezi presentation on the respiratory system:

https://prezi.com/-mnkf9ku66um/respiration-aerobic-v-anaerobic

Assessment preparation

Think about the tasks that your teacher may set you to assess your knowledge of the musculo-skeletal and cardio-respiratory systems, their functions and roles. Make sure you:

- know the key components of the musculo-skeletal system:
  - major bones
  - skeletal muscle groups
  - synovial joints
  - connective tissue
  - functions of the musculo-skeletal system during activity
- know the key components of the cardio-respiratory system and their function:
  - heart
  - respiratory system
  - blood
  - blood vessels
  - functions of the cardio-respiratory system during activity

- know the role of the musculo-skeletal system in producing movement:
  - types of movement
  - functions of connective tissue
  - types of muscle contractions
- know the role of the cardio-respiratory system during physical activity:
  - heart rate
  - blood pressure
  - vascular shunt mechanism
  - internal respiration
  - aerobic and anaerobic respiration.

You will need to include many relevant sporting examples.

Mark scheme

LO1: Know the key components of the musculo-skeletal and cardio-respiratory systems, their functions and roles		
Mark band 1	Mark band 2	Mark band 3
Locates and identifies **some** key components of the musculo-skeletal system and its functions. Description of the key components and functions of the cardio-respiratory system is **basic**.	Locates and identifies **many** key components of the musculo-skeletal system and its functions. Description of the key components and functions of the cardio-respiratory system is **detailed**.	Locates and identifies **most** key components of the musculo-skeletal system and its functions. Description of the key components and functions of the cardio-respiratory system is **comprehensive**.
Mark band 1	Mark band 2	Mark band 3
Outlines the role of the musculo-skeletal system in producing movement. **Outlines** the role of the cardio-respiratory system in physical activity.	**Describes** the role of the musculo-skeletal system in producing movement, supported with a **range** of examples. **Describes** the role of the cardio-respiratory system in physical activity supported with a **range** of examples.	**Comprehensively describes** the role of the musculo-skeletal system in producing movement, supported with a **wide range** of examples. **Comprehensively describes** the role of the cardio-respiratory system in physical activity supported with a **wide range** of examples.

LO2 Understand the importance of the musculo-skeletal and cardio-respiratory systems in health and fitness

Benefits of cardio-respiratory fitness in everyday life

Cardio-respiratory fitness is defined as the ability of the circulatory and respiratory systems to supply oxygen to muscles during sustained physical activity. Exercising regularly reduces the risk of heart disease, obesity, some cancers and strokes. Exercise also reduces stress.

> **Read about it**
>
> Benefits of regular exercise:
>
> **www.nhs.uk/live-well/exercise/exercise-health-benefits**
>
> **www.healthline.com/nutrition/10-benefits-of-exercise#section2**

Reducing the risk of heart disease

Heart disease is the term that describes what happens when your heart's blood supply is blocked or interrupted by a build-up of fatty substances in the coronary arteries that supply the heart with blood.

Over time, the walls of your arteries can become furred up with these fatty deposits. A **heart attack** occurs when these fatty deposits limit the supply of blood and part of the heart dies through lack of oxygen.

The build-up of fatty deposits in the arteries is part of our 'western' way of life in terms of diet and lifestyle. People who do not take care of their bodies are more likely to have fatty deposits in their coronary arteries and, therefore, suffer heart attacks.

There is no single cause of a heart attack. Doctors are unable to predict whether a person will have a heart attack. What has been found, however, is that certain people are more at risk of a heart attack than others.

Risk factors include:

- high levels of cholesterol in the blood
- high blood pressure
- diabetes
- hereditary predisposition (heart attacks often run in families)
- obesity
- advanced age.

Regular exercise will improve your cardio-respiratory fitness and can help to prevent heart disease. Your heart is a muscle and, like all muscles, it gets stronger and healthier if you exercise it regularly. People who do not exercise are almost twice as likely to get heart disease as people who are active. The British Heart Foundation recommends 2.5 hours of moderate intensity exercise each week.

> **Getting started**
>
> Research the benefits of exercise for the heart and lungs.

> **Key term**
>
> **Heart disease** Build-up of fatty deposits in the coronary arteries that limits the supply of blood to the heart, leading to a heart attack.

Reducing the risk of obesity

Obesity is a term used to describe people with excess body fat (usually over 40 per cent body fat). It is caused by a complex combination of lifestyle choices (eating more food than you use up through exercise), genetics, metabolic factors and socioeconomic factors. Some medications and diseases can also cause a person's weight to increase.

It may seem obvious, but carrying a large fat content can affect performance. Although performance in some activities can actually improve due to a large fat content – for example sumo wrestling – the effect of being obese is generally negative as it can limit different components of a person's fitness.

Obesity can affect fitness by:

- limiting stamina, which makes it difficult to perform activities of a long duration
- limiting flexibility, which makes it difficult for performers to use a full range of movement at joints when attempting to perform skills
- limiting agility and speed, which makes it difficult to move quickly.

Obesity also has negative effects on a person's health and well-being. It can cause ill-health because it:

- contributes to the development of cancer
- contributes to heart disease
- contributes to an increase in blood pressure
- contributes to the development of diabetes
- can lead to injury
- can lead to stress.

One of the main benefits of exercise is that it can prevent or reduce obesity. This is because exercise involves using energy. This energy comes from the food we eat, or from our fat stores. If it comes from the fat stores obesity will be reduced.

Reducing the risk of cancer

Scientists have shown that people who are physically active are less likely to develop some cancers. Because exercise has several biological effects on the body, it is thought that these may in some way stop the development of certain cancers.

Reucing the risk of strokes

A **stroke** happens when the blood supply to part of your brain is cut off, causing brain cells to become damaged or die because they do not get the oxygen and nutrients they need from your blood. This can affect your speech, as well as the way you think and move.

A stroke has the same potential causes as a heart attack – high cholesterol levels, high blood pressure, diabetes, obesity, family history and age.

Key terms

Obesity The state of being very overweight; where more than 40 per cent of body mass is fat.

Stroke A life-threatening medical condition caused by a lack of blood supply to part of the brain.

Figure 3.31 Obesity can limit participation in physical activity and be harmful to health

Reducing stress

Studies show that exercising regularly can positively affect mental health and well-being, by reducing **stress** levels. Exercise reduces the levels of the body's stress hormones, such as adrenaline, and stimulates production of endorphins – hormones that reduce pain and boost pleasure.

 Group activity

A local fitness club wants to encourage more of the community to improve their health and fitness. Create an advertisement detailing the benefits of cardio-respiratory fitness.

Figure 3.32 Stress can limit participation and be harmful to health

Benefits of muscular strength and flexibility

Exercise can improve many aspects of fitness, including muscular strength and flexibility.

Muscular strength relates to the force that can be produced by a muscle or group of muscles, and there are different ways that this force can be applied:

- **Maximal strength** is the largest force possible in a single maximal contraction.
- **Dynamic strength** is concerned with repeated contractions.
- **Explosive strength** is also known as power; it is the product of strength and speed.
- **Static strength** is the application of muscular strength against something that does not move. For example, in rugby when both teams push with the same force in a scrum and the scrum is not moving, the muscles apply a force but no movement occurs.

Flexibility is the range of movement possible at a joint. Different joints in the body have different ranges of movement, depending on the type of joint being used, for example a ball and socket joint allows a wider range of movement than a hinge joint.

Completing everyday tasks with ease

Improved muscular strength and flexibility will enable individuals to complete everyday tasks with ease.

For example, increased muscular strength will making walking up several flights of stairs easier; it will also make lifting and carrying heavy items such as suitcases easier.

Improved flexibility will enable individuals to stretch and reach further. It will make tying up shoes easier, for example.

Stretch activity

A medical doctor is concerned about the cardio-respiratory fitness of their older patients. Create an information leaflet listing how cardio-respiratory fitness can be beneficial for everyday life.

 Key terms

Stress Emotional strain or tension.
Muscular strength The ability of a muscle or group of muscles to exert force.

Avoiding injury

Improving muscular strength and flexibility through training is very effective at helping to avoid injury for a variety of reasons.

Strength training not only improves the strength of the muscles, but also of the tendons, ligaments and bones. Stronger muscles and tendons help hold the body in proper alignment and protect the bones and joints when moving or under impact. Bones become stronger and the ligaments become more flexible and better at absorbing the shock applied to them during sporting movements.

Injuries are sometimes caused through muscle imbalance, where an area of the body that is used less during an activity may become weak compared to other areas; when that area is called into play suddenly during an activity, it cannot handle the sudden stress placed on it and an injury occurs. Strength training will remove these weak areas and balance the body for the activities it is called to do.

Developing good flexibility is beneficial as it can prevent individuals from getting an injury. For example, if a person moves their body out of the normal range of movement, a muscle strain could occur. With improved flexibility, an individual will improve their range of movement and so be less likely to get injured by overstretching.

Improving posture

Increased muscular strength and flexibility can improve posture and help prevent injuries (see Unit R041, pages 12–15).

Injuries caused by postural defects such as pelvis tilt, kyphosis, lordosis and scoliosis are generally due to muscle imbalance, which can lead to strains or sprains.

Improved muscular strength and flexibility can reduce the likelihood of injuries occurring by helping to counteract muscle imbalance.

> ### Links to other units
> The information in Unit R042 LO2 is useful when considering the effect of strength on posture.

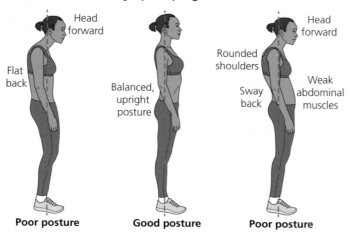

Head forward
Flat back
Balanced, upright posture
Head forward
Rounded shoulders
Sway back
Weak abdominal muscles

Poor posture   **Good posture**   **Poor posture**

Figure 3.33 Increased muscular strength and flexibility can improve posture and help prevent injuries

Preventing joint problems and osteoporosis in later life

Strength training and flexibility training can help to prevent joint problems and osteoporosis in later life.

Strength training and flexibility training help improve muscle imbalances. Muscle imbalances create an abnormal pull on a joint, causing it to move in an unnatural pattern. Stronger muscles on one side of a joint will cause it to pull in one direction, resulting in a stretching of the ligaments on the opposite side of the joint and a tightening of the ones on the same side as the strong muscle. This can lead to chronic joint pain and an unnatural wearing of the bones. A balanced strength-training programme will help to prevent these effects by strengthening the weaker muscles in order to balance them with the stronger ones.

Flexibility training can also help to prevent joint problems and osteoporosis because regular exercise stimulates the ligaments, muscles and tendons surrounding joints to strengthen and tighten.

Osteoporosis is a disease in which bones become increasingly weak as people get older. It is the most common reason for a broken bone among the elderly and is caused by a loss of minerals from the bones, which makes them become fragile. There are typically no symptoms until a fracture occurs. Bones may weaken to such a degree that a break may occur with relatively minor stress.

Exercise can help to prevent osteoporosis and a loss of bone strength. Strength training not only strengthens muscles but also increases bone density, making the bones stronger and less likely to fracture. Indeed, strength training actually increases the mineral content of bones.

Benefits of muscular endurance

Muscular endurance is the ability of a muscle or group of muscles to undergo repeated contractions while avoiding fatigue. The benefits of muscular endurance include increased **cardiovascular endurance** (stamina) for work-based tasks and improved sport skill performance.

Increased stamina for work-based tasks

People with good muscular endurance can keep going even when their muscles are fatigued. This might be during an intense exercise programme, but it also could be digging in the garden or shovelling snow. Individuals with muscular endurance do not tire easily, especially when it comes to performing vigorous exertion or work-based tasks.

Improved sport skill performance

Good muscular endurance means that an individual can keep doing the same movement repeatedly, without fatigue. If this movement is a sports skill, the muscular endurance means that you can keep doing this skill when others may be too fatigued to continue. You would have improved sport skill performance.

Group activity

Imagine your classroom is on the fifteenth floor of the building and that you had to climb the stairs to get here. List ideas about how good muscular strength could help you perform this task.

Key term

Osteoporosis Weakening of the bones in older people.

Stretch activity

Explain the benefits of muscular strength and endurance to someone who is suffering from pain in their knee joints.

Know it!

1 Name four benefits of cardio-respiratory fitness in everyday life.
2 Name three benefits of muscular strength and flexibility.
3 Name two benefits of muscular endurance.

Links to other units

You can find further information on this topic in Units R041, R042, R045 and R046.

Read about it

Effects of exercise:

www.teachpe.com/anatomy/short_term_effects.php

Long- and short-term effects of exercise:

www.bbc.com/bitesize/guides/z367tyc/revision/1

Assessment preparation

Think about the tasks that your teacher may set you to assess your knowledge of the importance of the musculo-skeletal and cardio-respiratory systems in health and fitness. Make sure you:

- know the benefits of cardio-respiratory fitness in everyday life in preventing:
  - heart disease
  - obesity
  - some cancers
  - strokes
  - stress
- know the benefits of muscular strength and flexibility, such as:
  - completing everyday tasks with ease
  - avoiding injury
  - improving posture
  - preventing joint problems and osteoporosis
- know the benefits of muscular endurance, such as:
  - increased stamina for everyday life
  - improved sport skill performance.

You will need to know many relevant sporting examples.

Mark scheme

LO2: Understand the importance of the musculo-skeletal and cardio-respiratory systems in health and fitness		
Mark band 1	Mark band 2	Mark band 3
Identifies **some** benefits of cardio-respiratory fitness, muscular strength and endurance, and muscular flexibility, supported with a **few** examples.	**Describes a range** of benefits of cardio-respiratory fitness, muscular strength and endurance, and muscular flexibility, supported with **mostly relevant** examples.	**Describes accurately** and in **detail** a **wide range** of benefits of cardio-respiratory fitness, muscular strength and endurance, and muscular flexibility, supported with **clear and relevant** examples.

LO3   Be able to assess the short-term effects of physical activity on the musculo-skeletal and cardio-respiratory systems

Different short-term effects of physical activity on the musculo-skeletal and cardio-respiratory systems and reasons for these

The short-term effects of physical activity on the musculo-skeletal and cardio-respiratory systems include effects on joints, the heart, breathing, body temperature and muscle fatigue.

Changes in the range of movement around joints

Physical activity warms up the muscles involved in the activity and increases their elasticity. Movement also makes the ligaments surrounding joints more supple. Finally, the joints themselves release more synovial fluid to reduce friction during movement. Each of these short-term effects means that during exercise the range of movement around joints increases.

Changes in heart rate, stroke volume and cardiac output

When a performer begins to exercise, the body has to supply extra oxygen to the working muscles. In order to do that, the heart begins to beat faster. The normal resting **heart rate** is somewhere around 70 to 80 beats per minute, but it can vary considerably. Exercise can easily raise the heart rate to 100–150 beats per minute or even higher, depending on how hard the exercise is. The heart will also contract more powerfully during exercise, increasing the amount of blood pumped out of the heart with each contraction. This is the **stroke volume**.

Cardiac output is the volume of blood that the heart is able to pump out each minute and represents the volume of oxygenated blood that is delivered to the body. The increased heart rate and the increased stroke volume that occur during exercise mean that more blood is being pumped around the body to supply the muscles with the glucose and oxygen they need.

Heart rate usually increases before activity because of the expectation of exercise. This slight increase in heart rate before exercise is called the **anticipatory rise** and is caused by the release of the hormone adrenaline.

Cardiac output, heart rate and stroke volume are related as follows:

$$\text{cardiac output [Q]} = \text{heart rate [HR]} \times \text{stroke volume [SV]}$$

Getting started

Working with a partner, make a list of the short-term effects of exercise on health and fitness.

Group activity

Following on from the getting started activity, join with another pair and identify whether the effects that you have listed are on the musculo-skeletal or cardio-respiratory systems.

Links to other units

You will find the information in R042 to be useful for this topic.

Read about it

Heart rate measurements:

www.topendsports.com/testing/heart-rate-measure.htm

www.ptdirect.com/training-delivery/client-assessment/taking-heart-rate-measurements

Changes to breathing rate

A resting breathing rate is about 15 breaths per minute. When exercise begins, the breathing rate increases as well as the depth of breathing, which in turn increases the amount of air we breathe in and out with each breath. The increased rate and depth of breathing allows for greater gaseous exchange at the lungs, so more oxygen enters the blood and more carbon dioxide is breathed out.

Changes in body temperature

Another short-term effect of exercise is that body temperature increases, because the muscles are contracting more often which generates heat. This increase in temperature is noticeable by the way the body tries to control it and keep cool. The body begins to sweat to try to lose heat by the evaporation of sweat off the skin's surface. The skin also goes red as blood vessels near the skin's surface open to try to lose heat by radiation.

Muscle fatigue

During a short, intense burst of exercise such as sprinting, energy is generated anaerobically, or without oxygen. When the body works anaerobically it produces lactic acid as a waste product, and lactic acid produces muscle fatigue. The body needs extra oxygen during recovery after anaerobic exercise to remove the lactic acid that has been produced.

Ways to measure and record the short-term effects of physical activity on the musculo-skeletal and cardio-respiratory systems

It is often beneficial to measure the short-term effects of physical activity on the musculo-skeletal and cardio-respiratory systems, in order to identify any weaknesses and so advise which areas a performer needs to work on in training.

Group activity

Draw or print a large outline of the body. On this, highlight where the short-term effects of exercise may take place.

Stretch activity

On the body created for the group activity above, add details of how these effects are identified and measured.

Suitable activities to measure the short-term effects

The easiest way to measure the short-term effects of physical activity is to get somebody to undertake physical activity and measure the effects on that person. Suitable activities would be shuttle runs, or exercises such as a number of press-ups completed in a minute, from which we could measure any changes in heart rate or breathing rate. If the activity is water-based, then swimming widths or lengths would be the equivalent of shuttle runs.

Methods to measure the short-term effects

You can measure the short-term effects of physical activity by measuring heart rate and breathing rate before, during and after exercise.

Heart rate is measured as the number of heart beats per minute. You can measure heart rate at any spot on the body where an artery is close to the surface and a pulse can be felt. The most common places to measure heart rate are at the wrist (radial artery) and neck (carotid artery).

It is preferable to use a heart rate monitor, as this provides a more accurate heart rate measurement. Phone apps that can measure heart rate are also available.

It should be noted that heart rate varies depending on whether the person is standing, sitting or lying down. Lying down is probably the best position for accurate results.

Also remember the anticipatory rise. Give the person some time to relax before you measure their heart rate.

Breathing is measured in breaths per minute. To get an accurate measurement, have the person lie down. Use a stop watch or phone to time one minute and count the number of times the person's chest rises and falls during that minute. If you are pressed for time, count the number of breaths taken in 15 seconds and then multiply that number by four.

If you tell the person that you are going to measure their breathing, they are likely to change their breathing rate without realising it. Ask them to breathe normally. To improve the accuracy of your result, you should take the measurement three times and average the results.

Once the resting heart and breathing rates have been measured, the person should begin exercising. As previously mentioned, suitable activities could include shuttle runs, press-ups or star jumps, or doing these exercises for a certain duration as dictated by a suitably experienced teacher, coach or instructor.

After the exercise, the performer should lie down and their heart rate and breathing rate should be measured as before.

If using a heart rate monitor, you may be able to record the heart rate during the activity.

Group activity

Work with a partner. One person should lie down and the other should measure their breathing rate. Record three measurements to improve accuracy. Change roles and repeat.

Now do some exercise and then remeasure the breathing rates. Discuss any changes your note.

Recording the outcomes

The measurements of heart rate and breathing rate prior to, during and after exercise can be written down to record the outcomes of the physical activity.

Numbers and measurements such as heart rate and breathing rate are called **objective data**.

Key terms

Objective data Facts and numbers that can be measured.

Subjective data Opinions and thoughts.

The other short-term effects of physical activity, such as sweating, muscle fatigue and body temperature, are not normally measured objectively because of the difficulty in doing so. However, they can be measured subjectively. **Subjective data** involve opinions. You could ask the performer how tired they feel to get an idea of their level of muscle fatigue. You could look at their face and give an opinion of how much they have sweated or how red they look to provide subjective data on the effect of the physical activity on their body temperature.

Know it!

1 State four short-term effects of physical activity on the musculo-skeletal and cardio-respiratory systems.
2 Describe two ways of measuring the short-term effects of physical activity on the musculo-skeletal and cardio-respiratory systems.

Links to other units

You can find further information on this topic in Units R041, R042, R045 and R046.

Assessment preparation

Think about the tasks that your teacher may set you to assess the short-term effects of physical activity on the musculo-skeletal and cardio-respiratory systems. Make sure you:

- know the different short-term effects of physical activity on the musculo-skeletal and cardio-respiratory systems and the reasons for these:
  - changes in the range of movement around joints
  - changes in heart rate, stroke volume and cardiac output
  - changes to breathing rate
  - changes in temperature
  - muscle fatigue
- know ways to measure and record the short-term effects:
  - suitable activities to measure the short-term effects
  - methods to measure the short-term effects
  - recording the outcomes.

You will need to explain the adaptations that occur.

You will need to use relevant information from other units, such as R042, R044, R045 and R046.

Mark scheme

LO3: Be able to assess the short-term effects of physical activity on the musculo-skeletal and cardio-respiratory systems		
Mark band 1	**Mark band 2**	**Mark band 3**
The short-term effects of physical activity on the musculo-skeletal and cardio-respiratory systems are identified, measured and recorded with **limited accuracy**. **Some** teacher support may be required in planning and setting up suitable activities. **Describes** the adaptations recorded and makes **basic suggestions** as to why they have occurred. Draws on **limited** skills/knowledge/understanding from other units in the specification.	The short-term effects of physical activity on the musculo-skeletal and cardio-respiratory systems are identified, measured and recorded **accurately**. **Little** teacher support may be required in planning and setting up suitable activities. **Describes** the adaptations recorded and provides **some explanation** as to why they have occurred. Draws on **some relevant** skills/knowledge/understanding from other units in the specification.	The short-term effects of physical activity on the musculo-skeletal and cardio-respiratory systems are identified, measured and recorded **precisely**. Planning and setting up suitable activities are carried out **independently**. **Fully explains** the adaptations recorded and why they have occurred. Draws on **relevant** skills/knowledge/understanding from other units in the specification.

LO4 Be able to assess the long-term effects of physical activity on the musculo-skeletal and cardio-respiratory systems

Long-term effects of physical activity on the musculo-skeletal and cardio-respiratory systems and reasons for these

If sport and physical activity are undertaken regularly, they will have long-term effects on the musculo-skeletal and cardio-respiratory systems. These changes may take months before they become measurable.

Changes in muscle size and strength

The effects of regular training on muscles depend to a certain extent on the type of exercise undertaken. Aerobic exercise will lead to an increase in muscular endurance (the muscles can keep contracting without fatigue for longer).

There will also be an increase in muscle size and strength with regular anaerobic exercise. This increase in the size of muscles – **muscle hypertrophy** – is especially pronounced with weight training.

Changes in resting heart rate

A long-term training programme will mean that the heart is beating at a higher rate than normal for long periods of time. The heart is a muscle and, like any other muscle exposed to regular intense exercise, it will increase in size. In other words, hypertrophy of the heart will occur. This increased size of the heart means that it can contract with greater force and pump out more blood with each beat. In other words, the stroke volume of the heart increases because of regular exercise.

Note that long-term exercise does not cause significant changes to the size of the body: the skeleton remains the same shape and size, as do all the major organs. Therefore, the amount of blood that the body needs when not exercising remains essentially the same. The amount of blood that the body receives depends on the cardiac output. Remember that:

cardiac output = stroke volume × heart rate

So, at rest, the cardiac output of a hypertrophied heart remains unchanged, but the stroke volume increases because of repeated exercise. This means that the **resting heart rate must reduce** to produce the same resting cardiac output. This reduction in resting heart rate in performers who have undertaken months or years of regular exercise is called **bradycardia**.

Changes in training heart rate

Regular exercise has the long-term effect of increasing stroke volume, so the heart of a person who has been exercising regularly pumps out more blood with each beat.

This means that this person's heart needs to beat less frequently to deliver the same cardiac output both at rest and during exercise. A person who has trained regularly has a **lower training heart rate** than another person who has not been training regularly. Changes in training heart rate may be measured objectively.

Table 3.1 The effect of regular training on heart rate

	Resting heart rate (beats per minute)	Exercising heart rate (beats per minute)
Average participant	80	140
Participant who trains regularly	55	110

Changes in heart rate recovery

The heart rate recovers back to its resting levels much more quickly as a result of long-term training. Not only does the heart rate return to normal quickly, but most of the recovery is in the first few minutes after finishing the exercise. Changes in heart rate recovery may be measured objectively.

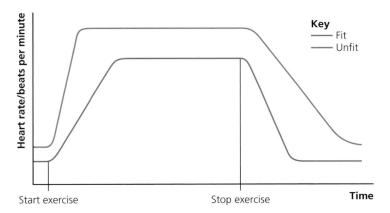

Figure 3.34 The effects of exercise on heart rate and heart rate recovery

Changes in flexibility

Regular training brings about changes in flexibility. Because they are being used more often, muscles, tendons and ligaments around joints become stronger. This helps improve the stability of the joints, but also increases the flexibility at joints. More flexibility means an increased range of movement. Because of training, performers are able to stretch and reach further without injuring themselves. Changes in flexibility can be measured objectively by performing flexibility tests.

Changes in muscle recovery

Exercise involves movement, and movement means muscles need to contract. Repeated muscle contractions produce waste products such as lactic acid that can cause fatigue. This fatigue is what causes the tiredness felt during exercise and may make performers slow down or even stop. Also, after strenuous exercise there is sometimes a delayed soreness that occurs in muscles a day or two later.

A long-term training effect is that muscle recovery becomes quicker, as the muscles do not become as fatigued as previously. This is because the body produces less lactic acid and is better able to cope with any lactic acid that is produced. Also, because the muscles get used to exercise, there is less likelihood of delayed muscle soreness occurring. Changes in muscle recovery may be measured subjectively.

Changes in lung capacity

Lung capacity is the amount of air your lungs can hold. The amount of air you breathe in and out at rest is known as the **tidal volume**. In contrast, when you take a deep breath and then exhale, the amount of air expelled from your lungs is known as the **vital capacity**. Regular exercise makes your body more efficient at transporting and using oxygen, making the vital capacity slightly bigger and exercise less difficult than for someone who is not training regularly.

The biggest difference between individuals who train and those who do is not changes in lung capacity, but rather the ability of the heart to pump oxygen-rich blood to different muscle groups, and the ability of the muscles to extract oxygen from the blood.

Changes in lung capacity may be measured objectively.

Key terms

Lung capacity Amount of air your lungs can hold.

Tidal volume Amount of air you breathe in and out at rest.

Vital capacity Amount of air expelled from your lungs when you take a deep breath and then exhale fully.

Ways to measure and record the long-term effects of physical activity on the musculo-skeletal and cardio-respiratory systems

Many of the effects of regular training are not seen for months or even years after training has started. This is because the changes are to the actual structure of the body to allow the various systems of the body to work more efficiently during exercise.

Rather than rely on memory, it is easier to measure and record the long-term effects of physical activity on the musculo-skeletal and cardio-respiratory systems.

These measures can produce both objective and subjective data.

Suitable long-term activities to bring about adaptations

There is no 'correct' method of improving somebody's fitness. Similarly, there is no suitable timescale to bring about specified adaptations. It all depends on the individual concerned. So, there is no single, suitable long-term activity to bring about adaptations.

The type of activity chosen, and the duration of the activity, depends on specifics such as the age of the performer, the availability of facilities, the level of commitment/motivation, specific weaknesses to be developed and so on.

The first thing to do is to gather information about the individual, such as their age, reasons for wanting to get fit, any current or recent injuries, any health problems, their level of sporting involvement, any likes or dislikes regarding training methods, and what facilities are easily available to them.

The next thing to do is to find out which components of fitness they need to improve. This will often depend on the reason why the individual wants to get fit, for example improving general fitness, trying to lose weight, to take part in a cycling event or to run a local 5K fun run.

Think about the components of fitness listed in Unit R042, pages 43–5, and decide which components are most needed for the activity in question. You need to use appropriate fitness tests (also in Unit R042) to determine the individual's level of fitness, and to occasionally repeat those tests to monitor progress during the training programme.

The next stage is to decide on a training program using the FITTA principles (Unit R042, page 36).

You should start at a level that the performer finds relatively easy and gradually increase the workload. It is usual to increase the workload by about ten per cent each session.

If the training is primarily aerobic, involving constant running, cycling or swimming, the sessions should last for 20–40 minutes. Anaerobic, strength-based or circuit training sessions should last 15–30 minutes. Both types of exercise should be undertaken three times a week, with 48 hours' recovery between sessions.

The programme should be planned in repeating four-week cycles. In the first three weeks, the workload should increase each week to build fitness levels. The fourth week should comprise active recovery and tests to monitor progress and to inform adjustments to the training program.

The following four-week cycle should build up to a higher level of fitness over three weeks, followed by further tests and adjustments.

The programme needs to last 12–16 weeks in order to see any adaptations occur, and both the initial planning and subsequent adjustments should be discussed with the performer to ensure the programme is enjoyable and convenient to do.

Methods to measure the long-term effects

The various adaptations that occur as a result of training, such as changes in heart rate, breathing rate and muscle strength, have been discussed previously. You need to use various methods to measure these long-term effects.

Increases in muscle size can be shown by using a tape measure to measure the girth of muscles. The usual muscles to measure are the quadriceps and hamstrings in the thigh, and the biceps and triceps in the arm.

Increases in muscle strength can be shown using weightlifting exercises to see any improvements in how much weight a performer can lift or how many times a weight can be lifted.

Changes to heart rate may be measured using a heart rate monitor or by taking the pulse rate. The heart rate should be measured at rest, during exercise and during recovery.

Changes in flexibility can be measured using a type of protractor called a **goniometer**, which measures the angle through which a joint can be moved.

Changes in lung capacity can be measured using a **spirometer**, which is a small machine attached by a cable to a mouthpiece. The performer is seated, and a soft clip is placed on their nose to stop air escaping from it.

For the test, the performer inhales fully, to completely fill the lungs with air, and is then asked to exhale as quickly and forcefully as they can, making sure they empty their lungs fully. The test is normally repeated at least three times to ensure a reliable result.

A simpler way is to measure the vital capacity using a balloon. To do this, stretch a round balloon several times to make it easier to inflate. Take a deep breath and then exhale into the balloon. Pinch the end of the balloon and measure its diameter in centimetres. Convert the diameter to volume using the graph shown in Figure 3.37 and record the result.

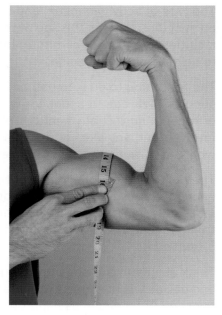
Figure 3.35 Measuring muscle girth

Figure 3.36 A goniometer

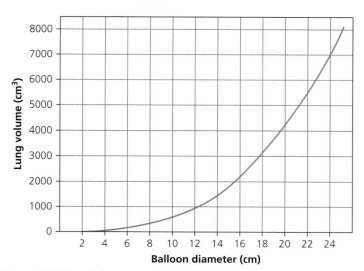
Figure 3.37 Graph for measuring vital capacity using a balloon

The **Cooper run test** can measure the long-term effects of exercise on aerobic capacity. The test is described in Unit R042, page 67. It has the advantage of being able to measure the aerobic fitness of large groups all at once, and is a very cheap and simple test to perform.

Recording the outcomes and subjective measures

All the measurements given above produce objective data that could be recorded on a data recording sheet.

You could also make a subjective measurement of how well the performer feels that their muscles are recovering, or whether the performer feels that their stamina or strength are improving.

Comparing the retest results with the initial tests will identify any adjustments that may need to be made to the training programme.

It is important to repeat the same specific **standard tests** to check for improvement against the performer's previous results and to compare their results with **national norms**, both throughout and at the end of the programme.

A diary can be used to help monitor the programme, recording details of how you feel it is progressing, where it has been adapted and any problems you may have encountered. A training diary method is a valuable tool for monitoring performance, as it enables performers to be actively involved in recording and monitoring their training activities. It should be completed after each training session.

Physical Fitness Log

Name				Rank	Sex (circle) M F		Organisation		
Week	Date	Phase of training	Exercise activity 1	Reps/time/ distance etc.	Heart rate attained	Exercise activity 2	Reps/time/ distance etc.	Heart rate attained	

INSTRUCTIONS
Record each workout including the date, phase of training, activities performed and heart rate attained. Note the repetitions/time/distance, or other indication of performance, for each activity.

Figure 3.38 Physical fitness log

Know it!

1 State six long-term effects of physical activity on the musculo-skeletal and cardio-respiratory systems.

2 Describe two ways of measuring the long-term effects of physical activity on the musculo-skeletal and cardio-respiratory systems.

Links to other units

You can find further information on this topic in Units R042, R045 and R046.

Assessment preparation

Think about the tasks that your teacher may set you to assess the long-term effects of physical activity on the musculo-skeletal and cardio-respiratory systems. Make sure you:

- know the long-term effects of physical activity on the musculo-skeletal and cardio-respiratory systems and the reasons for these, including changes in:
  - muscle size and strength
  - resting heart rate
  - training heart rate
  - heart rate recovery
  - flexibility
  - muscle recovery
  - lung capacity
- know ways to measure and record the long-term effects of physical activity on the musculo-skeletal and cardio-respiratory systems:
  - suitable long-term activities to bring about adaptations
  - methods to measure the long-term effects
  - recording the outcomes.

You will need to explain the adaptations that occur.

Mark scheme

LO4: Be able to assess the long-term effects of physical activity on the musculo-skeletal and cardio-respiratory systems		
Mark band 1	Mark band 2	Mark band 3
The long-term effects of physical activity on the musculo-skeletal and cardio-respiratory systems are identified, measured and recorded occasionally with **limited accuracy**. **Some** teacher support may be required in planning and setting up suitable activities.	The long-term effects of physical activity on the musculo-skeletal and cardio-respiratory systems are identified, measured and recorded **accurately** and with some regularity. **Little** teacher support may be required in planning and setting up suitable activities.	The long-term effects of physical activity on the musculo-skeletal and cardio-respiratory systems are identified, measured and recorded **precisely** and at **regular**, set **intervals**. Planning and setting up suitable activities are carried out **independently**.
Describes the adaptations recorded and makes **basic suggestions** as to why they have occurred.	**Describes** the adaptations recorded and provides **some explanation** as to why they have occurred.	**Fully explains** the adaptations recorded and why they have occurred.

R044 Sports psychology

About this unit

Within this unit, you will start to appreciate some of the finer details that make a difference in determining the success or failure of a performer. By identifying and exploring the many psychological factors that affect performance, you will gain knowledge and understanding of how such factors can be controlled and/or used to provide an advantage.

Factors to be studied include different personality types, increasing motivation, and the effect of aggression. Further study will investigate: the effects of varying levels of arousal and anxiety; setting appropriate, SMART motivational goals; and how to use relaxation techniques to remain calm, focused and at optimal performance levels.

The unit will allow you to develop your knowledge and understanding of some of the psychological strategies and techniques that can be used in the pursuit of excellence.

Learning outcomes

LO1 Understand the relationship between personality and sports performance

LO2 Know how motivation can affect sports performance

LO3 Know how aggression can affect sports performance

LO4 Understand the impact of arousal and anxiety on sports performance

LO5 Be able to apply sport psychology strategies to enhance sports performance

How will I be assessed?

This is an optional unit. If selected, you will be assessed over 30 guided learning hours. Approximately ten hours of internal assessment will be worth 60 marks (60 UMS). OCR provides a model assignment to follow. This unit is centre assessed and OCR moderated.

OCR provides a model assignment for this unit: http://ocr.org.uk/qualifications/cambridge-nationals/cambridge-nationals-sport-science-level-1-2-j802-j812/assessment

For LO1

You need to have knowledge and understanding of:
- personality types
- how personality can affect performance and choices
- the difference between trait and social learning theory.

For LO2

You need to have knowledge and understanding of:
- types of motivation
- the effect of motivation on performance
- achievement motivation and how it affects performance.

For LO3

You need to have knowledge and understanding of:
- types of aggression
- reasons for aggression
- theories that explain aggression.

For LO4

You need to have knowledge and understanding of:
- arousal
- theories relating to arousal
- ways to measure anxiety in sport.

For LO5

You need to have knowledge and understanding of:
- the use of goal setting for motivation in sport
- the use of mental rehearsal, imagery and relaxation techniques
- how to assess whether strategies have had an impact on sports performance.

LO1 Understand the relationship between personality and sports performance

Getting started

Imagine you are writing a tweet to post on Twitter that describes your personality. Write down your tweet, describing the main characteristics of your personality. Do not write your name on it. Fold the paper up and place it in a box. When everyone is finished, pick out one of the pieces of paper and try to guess who in your class is being described.

Definitions of personality

Personality can be defined as the total number of unique characteristics of a person that distinguish them from other people, forming their character. A personality is made up of a person's **traits** – the distinguishing characteristics that typically belong to one person. If you know what these traits are, to an extent you can predict how the person might behave in certain situations.

 Key terms

Personality The total number of unique characteristics of a person that distinguish them from other people, forming their character.

Traits Distinguishing characteristics that typically belong to a person, which make up their personality.

It is debatable whether personality is set and inherited, learned through experiences or a mixture of both. What is known is that a performer's personality plays a large part in the way they behave in different situations. Examples include:

- whether we are generally calm or nervous
- whether we are outgoing or shy
- whether we avoid or embrace competition
- whether we accept or reject responsibility.

Extrovert and introvert personality types

Two common ways to categorise personality is to classify performers as either **extrovert** or **introvert**. Although most people show a balance of some extrovert and introvert personality traits, it is possible to show more of one type than the other. The main differences between being classed as an extrovert or introvert are:

- whether a performer feels content in their own company or needs others to excite and arouse them
- how excited (aroused) they need to be to perform tasks.

Extrovert personality type

Performers with an extreme extrovert personality have distinctive characteristics, as shown in Figure 4.1.

 Key terms

Extrovert Personality type characterised by being sociable, outgoing and talkative, needing high arousal levels and being prone to boredom; extroverts tend to perform team sports.

Introvert Personality type characterised by shyness, concentration, thoughtfulness and low arousal levels; introverts tend to perform individual sports.

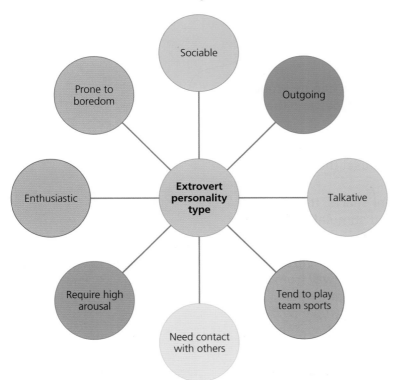

Figure 4.1 Extrovert personality type

Introvert personality type

Performers with an extreme introvert personality have distinctive characteristics, as shown in Figure 4.2.

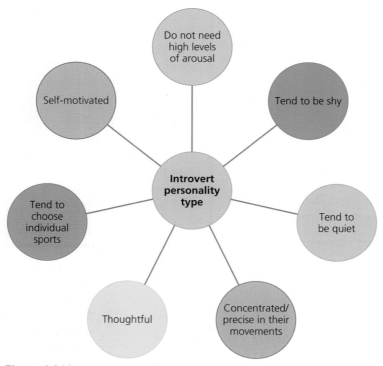

Figure 4.2 Introvert personality type

Links between personality and involvement and performance in sport

Although there are obvious exceptions to the rule, it can be argued that there are links between different personality types and their choice of activities, for example:

- Extreme extroverts tend to choose team sports, where others around them provide the stimulation and arousal they need to perform well.

- Extreme introverts tend to choose individual sports; they are happy in their own company and do not need stimulation or arousal from others to perform well.

Remember, however, that performers with an introvert personality type may well play team sports, but will simply shy away from too much attention from the media, the crowds or from other performers. Equally, extrovert personality types may take part in some form of individual activity but crave the attention, media coverage and crowd interaction that can come with that sport. For example, some golfers wear extravagant clothing and enjoy being the centre of attention, even though their sport is individual in its nature, e.g. Ian Poulter.

Figure 4.3 Archery is a sport that requires concentration and precise control; archers tend to demonstrate some introvert personality characteristics

Figure 4.4 Team sports such as football tend to be played by performers who demonstrate some extrovert personality characteristics

Group activity

Some examples of sports performers who have displayed aspects of introvert or extrovert personality types are given below. Conduct some research using the internet, **social media** and YouTube to find other examples.

Extrovert examples

Ronnie O'Sullivan is a snooker player. Although snooker is an individual sport, Ronnie has shown aspects of an extrovert personality type, enjoying media attention and playing at a fast pace – earning him the nickname 'The Rocket'.

When performing in the 100 m, Usain Bolt often showed extrovert personality characteristics. He had a very overt routine of playing to the crowd and seeking attention for his incredible performances. Clearly the 100 m is a fast-paced event.

Introvert examples

You can argue that Lionel Messi has showed more introvert personality characteristics than his rival Cristiano Ronaldo. Messi has not demanded the same media attention as Ronaldo and has attempted to stay out of the limelight, allowing his football to make his public statements.

Michael Jordan is one of the most famous basketball players of all time. However, his character tended to show more introvert personality characteristics. For example, he was quiet, relatively shy in front of the media, and protective of his private life.

Classroom discussion

As a class, compile a list of sporting activities that you feel extreme extroverts and introverts might choose to take part in. Also, discuss whether you feel you personally show more introvert or extrovert characteristics within your personality.

Key term

Social media Computer-based technologies that facilitate the creation and sharing of information and ideas via virtual communities and networks, for example Twitter, Facebook and Instagram.

The trait approach

In describing where a person's personality comes from, one approach suggests that a person's traits are set from birth. Trait theory suggests that a personality is:

- inherited (from parents)
- stable (does not change much)
- enduring (lasts forever).

The trait approach suggests that we are born with our personality characteristics and that these are relatively set for life. Such characteristics may provide advantages in certain sporting situations. Some examples are given in Table 4.1.

Table 4.1 Personality traits and their potential advantage in sport

Trait/characteristic	Potential advantage in sport
Aggressive	A certain level of aggression is needed in martial arts and in boxing to aggressively attack an opponent
Quiet/high concentration	Sports such as pistol shooting and archery require high levels of concentration
Talkative	A captain or leader in any sporting situation must be able to communicate with their team
Patient	A high level of patience is required in sports such as shooting
Brave	Bravery is a trait that is required to be a downhill skier, descending at high speed and with high risk

It can be argued that you can predict a performer's behaviour as a result of understanding their traits. For example, a naturally aggressive performer is likely to be particularly aggressive in highly aroused situations.

Observed or social learning

Social learning theory provides another explanation as to how our personalities develop. In this theory, personalities develop through our experiences and observations. This is particularly the case when we observe people that we admire or aspire to be like. Those people often gain a lot of recognition or attention from others and become role models.

However, it is important to note that social learning can only take place in the environment in which we live and which we experience. Thus, performers will only learn and copy from the people that they see and interact with. We copy the behaviours of those we are aware of and adjust our personalities in an attempt to be like them. This can work in a positive or negative manner. Examples are given below:

- If a young tennis player views an elite player complaining about a line call, they may copy this and do the same during their match.
- If a young athlete sees the dedication and commitment that an elite athlete puts into their training, they may copy this behaviour and work hard to achieve success.
- If a footballer views an elite performer diving during a match, they might deem this acceptable behaviour and copy them when they play.
- If a rugby player witnesses elite players respecting the referee's decision, they may do the same when they play.

 Key term

Social learning theory
A theory about how we develop our personality by watching and copying others.

Observational learning as part of social learning is summarised in Figure 4.5. We observe others and copy them, particularly if their behaviour is successful and rewarded. This involves watching and attending to a performance that we find satisfying and attractive. We retain this information and work out if we have the ability to reproduce what we have seen. We also work out if it is motivating to copy them: what will we gain? If we feel it is worthwhile, we may well act out what we have seen, particularly if we feel the action will be praised and reinforced.

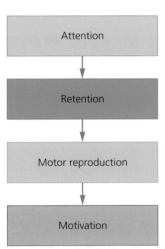

Figure 4.5 Observational learning as part of social learning.

Figure 4.6 When he was playing rugby, Jonny Wilkinson's pre-kick pose was copied all round the world as a desirable position in which to prepare to kick

Stretch activity

1   Name five different sports performers and try to describe their personalities, linking their characteristics to their choice of activity.

2   Conduct an interview with a local sports performer. Try to find out if they believe their personality is inherited (trait theory), learned (social learning theory), or a mixture of both.

 Group activity

Discuss and research elite sports performers to suggest examples of social learning, that is, where performers have clearly watched and copied other performers.

Know it!

1   Define what is meant by 'personality'.

2   Describe what sporting activities extreme introverts and extreme extroverts would tend to choose to perform in. Justify your answers.

3   Describe how performers in sport may show signs of introvert and extrovert personality characteristics in their sporting lives.

4   Using your knowledge of trait and social learning theories, give examples of how sports people may be naturally suited to, or learn to behave like performers in, certain sports.

Links to other units

You can find further information on this topic in Units R042, R043, R045 and R046.

Read about it

Watch a Prezi presentation on extroverts and introverts:

https://prezi.com/3p4yqdjdrt0r/are-introverts-or-extroverts-more-likely-to-play-sports-and-what-sports

Read about introverts in sport:

www.ranker.com/list/athletes-who-are-introverts/people-in-sports

Twenty distinguishing sports personality traits of top athletes:

www.sports-management-degrees.com/top-personality-traits-of-high-performing-athletes

Assessment preparation

Think about the tasks that your teacher may set you to assess your knowledge of personality. Make sure you:

- know what personality is
- are clear about what is meant by
  - introvert
  - extrovert
  - trait theory
  - social learning theory.

How will you demonstrate the links between personality and involvement in sport, including relevant examples?

Mark scheme

LO1: Understand the relationship between personality and sports performance		
Mark band 1	Mark band 2	Mark band 3
Attempts to define personality are **limited**. **Some** different personality types and approaches are **briefly** described. Some **simple** examples of the links between personality and involvement and performance in sport are provided.	A **range** of definitions of personality are provided and there is **detailed** information on different personality types and approaches. Attempts **some explanation** of the links between personality and involvement and performance in sport, supported with **mostly relevant** examples.	A **wide range** of definitions of personality are provided and there is **comprehensive** information on different personality types and approaches. **Explains accurately** and in **detail** the links between personality and involvement and performance in sport, supported with **clear** and **relevant** examples.

LO2 Know how motivation can affect sports performance

Definitions of motivation

Motivation can be defined as the drive or desire to achieve something. As a term, motivation is used in many contexts:

Figure 4.7 Motivation

It can be argued that only certain types of people are motivated to participate in sport. Equally, only certain types of people are motivated to dedicate themselves to the training and commitment required to reach an elite standard of play.

Intrinsic motivation

One type of motivation is known as **intrinsic motivation**. This motivation comes from within a performer and is the internal drive to achieve something. It refers to personal pride, satisfaction, or a feeling of general achievement. Examples include:

● the pride gained by beating a personal best

● the desire to feel like you have performed well

● wanting to improve at a sport because you enjoy it, or simply want to get better at it

● satisfaction or pride from taking part, for example from completing the London Marathon.

Extrinsic motivation

Extrinsic motivation is the drive from a performer to achieve a tangible or intangible reward. It comes from a source external to the performer.

● Tangible rewards can be touched, for example a trophy, a certificate, money or a medal.

● Intangible rewards cannot be touched, for example praise from parents, a coach or spectators.

Key terms

Motivation The drive or desire to achieve something.

Intrinsic motivation Comes from within a performer; the internal drive to achieve something.

Extrinsic motivation The drive from a performer to achieve a tangible or intangible reward; it comes from a source external to the performer.

An extrinsic motivator, such as a trophy, provides motivation for the performer. For example, Olympic athletes may work hard with the main aim of achieving a medal. This may provide the motivation they need to train hard and to dedicate themselves to try to achieve that reward. Many ex-performers cherish their medals and trophies as the main reason why they dedicated their life to the sport.

A young performer in a PE lesson may try hard to please their PE teacher or coach. The intangible extrinsic motivator of praise may be enough to make them want to try hard.

It is generally believed by psychologists that an internal drive to achieve is stronger than the desire to win trophies and so on. However, the winning of a trophy or reward (extrinsic motivator) may also provide personal satisfaction (intrinsic motivator). It is also apparent that some sports performers appear to be motivated solely by money (an extrinsic reward).

Achievement motivation

Achievement motivation is how motivated a performer is to achieve, or their desire to succeed. It refers to a performer's approach to sporting situations and competitions. These approaches can be divided into two types:

- need to achieve (NACH)
- need to avoid failure (NAF).

Need to achieve (NACH)

A performer who approaches sporting situations with a **need to achieve (NACH)** is said to display 'approach behaviour'. NACH performers tend to show the characteristics outlined in Figure 4.9.

Figure 4.9 Need to achieve (NACH) characteristics

Figure 4.8 The extrinsic motivator of a tangible trophy may well provide the motivational incentive for performers to strive to achieve success

 Classroom discussion

Discuss current elite sports performers and what appears to motivate them.

 Key terms

Achievement motivation How motivated a performer is to achieve, or their desire to succeed.

Need to achieve (NACH) Personality that wants to win, accepts challenges and competition, and persists in the face of failure.

NACH performers approach competitions and sporting situations with a desire to do well. They want to win and often make sacrifices in their life to achieve their goals. They tend to be dedicated to training and enjoy others watching and judging them on their performance. They take great personal pride in how well they perform.

Figure 4.10 Chris Hoy is one of Team GB's greatest ever athletes, winning six Olympic gold medals; he showed approach (NACH) behaviour

Need to avoid failure (NAF)

Performers who show a **need to avoid failure (NAF)** personality type are often afraid of evaluation when losing or failing, and therefore avoid competitive, challenging circumstances. They tend to show the characteristics outlined in Figure 4.11.

 Key term

Need to avoid failure (NAF)
Personality that is afraid of evaluation when losing or failing, so often avoids competitive, challenging circumstances.

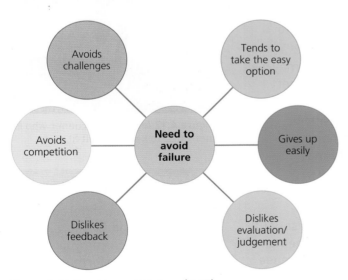

Figure 4.11 Need to avoid failure (NAF)

NAF characteristics can be shown by performers at different levels. Some examples are shown in Table 4.2.

Table 4.2 Examples of NAF characteristics

Scenario	Need to avoid failure characteristics
Amateur badminton player at a local leisure centre	Does not want to play against friends for fear of losing and being judged on their poor performance
Elite sprinter at the Olympics	Wants to be drawn against easy opponents in the rounds so they can qualify for the final
School performer playing in the local cup final	Feigns injury so they do not need to play, as many spectators will be there judging their performance
School PE performer playing tennis	May want to play easy opponents so that they know they will win; avoids better players

Implications for sport and exercise involvement

Motivation and personality play an important role in how people approach sporting activity, particularly in terms of:

- which sport/activities you choose to participate in
- how hard you try
- whether you keep trying or give up.

A very motivated performer may be happy to take part in as many activities as they can, or be dedicated to achieving excellence in one sport. Our level of motivation and the characteristics of our personality determine our choices and approaches to playing sport. Some examples are given below:

- A performer who is intrinsically motivated may decide to take part in an individual sport, as they are happy to train without others and can focus on their own performance and goals to be achieved.
- A performer who relies on others and external motivation may well decide to take part in a team sport. They may want the support and team spirit that comes from being with others, so they can collectively aim to achieve a trophy at the end of the season.
- Someone with approach (NACH) behaviour may be happy to set themselves very challenging goals. An athlete may want to win a medal at the Olympics and will meet the challenges of training and be happy to compete against the best performers.
- A school performer with a need to avoid failure (NAF) personality may decide not to attend county trials as they are happy being a good player in their own team and would not want to increase their chances of failure while being judged by scouts/coaches from a county team.
- A football player with extrinsic motivation may be happy not playing for the team as long as they receive their high wage at the end of the week.

Figure 4.12 An amateur runner who is motivated to keep herself fit

Stretch activity

Research three different elite sports performers. What evidence can you find in their performances that would suggest they are 'need to achieve' performers? Share your findings with a partner.

- A football player who is intrinsically motivated may decide to move clubs to play for a team that pays less than their previous club; their satisfaction with their performance is more important than the money they earn.
- Some people attend regular fitness classes, for example Zumba or spinning, as they are motivated to get or keep fit.
- Some people live sedentary lifestyles with little or no exercise as they are not motivated to get or keep fit.

Links to other units

You can find further information on this topic in Units R042, R043, R045 and R046.

Know it!

1 State what is meant by the term 'motivation'.
2 Give two examples of intrinsic motivation and two examples of extrinsic motivation.
3 Describe the difference between how a NACH performer approaches sport compared to a NAF performer.
4 Using your knowledge of motivation and achievement motivation, describe why performers may either choose or refuse to take part in an activity.

Read about it

What motivates athletes: **https://www.psychologytoday.com/ gb/blog/the-power-prime/200910/ sports-what-motivates-athletes**

Intrinsic versus extrinsic motivation:

http://sarahpavan.com/intrinsic-extrinsic-motivation

Assessment preparation

Think about the tasks that your teacher may set you to assess your knowledge of motivation. Make sure you:

- know what motivation is
- are clear about what is meant by:
  - ○ intrinsic motivation
  - ○ extrinsic motivation
  - ○ achievement motivation
  - ○ need to achieve and need to avoid failure.

How will you demonstrate how the main theories of motivation can be linked to a performer's choice of activity?

Mark scheme

LO2: Know how motivation can affect sports performance		
Mark band 1	Mark band 2	Mark band 3
Attempts to define motivation are **limited**. **Outlines** the main theories of motivation, supported with **some simple** examples of the implications for sport and exercise involvement.	A **range** of definitions of motivation are provided. **Describes** the main theories of motivation in **some detail**, supported with **mostly relevant** examples of the implications for sport and exercise involvement.	A **wide range** of definitions of motivation are provided. **Comprehensively describes** the main theories of motivation, supported with **clear** and **relevant** examples of the implications for sport and exercise involvement.

L03 Know how aggression can affect sports performance

Types of aggression

Aggressive acts are more common in some sporting activities than others. Sometimes aggression is a part of the sport itself; on other occasions, aggressive acts can be spontaneous and beyond the norms of that activity.

What is aggression?

Aggression is generally defined as deliberate behaviour against another person or object, which can be deemed positive or negative depending on whether it is controlled. Aggression is a deliberate, forceful act, which can be unpleasant or damaging but can also be a natural part of playing sport, for example aggressively tackling someone in rugby.

- If a performer is **positively aggressive** when boxing, they will strike their opponent to win, within the rules of the sport. This shows controlled aggression.

- If a performer is **negatively aggressive** in netball, they may well lead with their elbow to inflict a blow to their opponent's face, which is outside of the rules. This shows uncontrolled aggression.

Aggressive acts do not need to be physical. They can also be verbal with the intention of making the person receiving the aggressive abuse feel bad, e.g. the former French footballer Zinedine Zidane reacted with physical aggression after receiving verbal aggression from Marco Materazzi, in the 2006 World Cup Final.

Aggression can also be classified as direct and indirect.

Direct aggression

Direct aggression is any act that is directed at an opponent, performer or official with the intention of hurting them. Therefore, it is directly applied to that person. Examples include:

- going into a football tackle with the intention of harming the opponent
- going into a rugby tackle with extreme force to knock the opponent down in a violent manner
- barging into an opponent deliberately when dribbling a basketball
- throwing a punch below the belt in boxing with the intention of injuring the opponent
- verbally abusing a coach, using foul language
- verbally abusing an official when the performer does not agree with the decision given.

> **Getting started**
>
> Can you think of an elite sports performer who has shown acts of aggression? What reasons might explain why they were aggressive?

> 🔑 **Key term**
>
> **Direct aggression** Any act that is directed at an opponent, performer or official with the intention of hurting them.

Figure 4.13 When a performer aims to hurt another performer in football, this is direct aggression

Indirect aggression

Indirect aggression is when an act of frustration is aggressively directed towards a sporting object. Examples of indirect aggression include:

- smashing a golf club on the floor in frustration after playing a poor shot
- hitting a tennis racket off the floor in frustration after losing a point
- hitting a shuttlecock in badminton really hard
- kicking a football away in disgust at a referee's decision.

 Key term

Indirect aggression When an act of frustration is aggressively directed towards a sporting object.

Group activity

Look at the sporting examples given in Table 4.3. Decide which are examples of direct aggression and which are indirect aggression.

Table 4.3 Direct aggression or indirect aggression?

Sporting example	Direct aggression	Indirect aggression
A kick-boxer striking their opponent in the head with a swinging kick		
A high tackle in rugby league around the neck area		
Hitting a golf club on the ground in frustration		
Deliberately landing on an opponent's toes having jumped for a netball		
Hitting a hockey ball out of play in frustration		
Slamming a basketball to the floor in frustration at an official's decision		
Headbutting an opponent when playing handball		

Figure 4.14 Australian tennis player Sam Groth holding the racket he smashed on the floor after losing his match to Dudi Sela (indirect aggression)

Reasons for aggression

Although it can be argued that aggression is a natural reaction, common causes of aggression include rivalry, pressure to win, over-arousal during play, behaviour of the opposition and decisions of officials.

Rivalry

When opponents or teams are rivals, it can add an extra level of tension between the two parties when performing. Rivalry itself may be enough to cause a performer to carry out an aggressive act. Sometimes this is caused by frustration, desperation to win or because of pressure from others. Examples of rivalries that have resulted in aggressive acts include:

- **Boxing weigh-ins/press conferences**: boxing is often full of bravado and straight talking, but occasionally the rivalry between opponents can cause aggressive acts even before the real fight has taken place. In 2002, when Mike Tyson faced Lennox Lewis, Tyson threw a punch at the press conference and a brawl occurred. In 2012, Dereck Chisora threatened to shoot David Haye after the pair were involved in a press-conference fight after Chisora had lost to Vitali Klitschko.

- **National rivalry**: one of the oldest football rivalries of all, England versus Scotland, has resulted in some aggressive acts over the years, but there are many other incidents of national rivalries. Sometimes national pride and defiance to 'not lose to your rival' has proven the catalyst for violence. One of the worst examples was in 1946, which saw football teams Brazil and Argentina engage in fighting both with each other and the supporters attending the match.

> ### Read about it
>
> Read about football rivalries that have resulted in aggressive acts:
>
> www.theguardian.com/football/blog/2014/nov/17/football-international-rivalries-ranked-scotland-england

Pressure to win

The pressure to win can come from spectators, coaches, fellow players, sponsors and the media. It can cause performers to adopt a 'win at all costs' approach, potentially resulting in violent and aggressive acts. Examples include:

- pressure to win a cup final
- pressure to win a match or avoid defeat to prevent relegation or gain promotion
- local derby matches where the 'bragging rights' are deemed important, for example Newcastle versus Sunderland at football

- pressure to perform well to avoid losing sponsorship
- pressure from the coach to act aggressively, for example to foul an opponent who is playing well
- pressure from teammates to be seen to be joining in aggressive acts, for example if someone starts a punch up you may be pressurised to join in.

Over-arousal during play

Arousal is defined as a physiological and psychological state of excitement varying from deep sleep to intense excitement. Excitement levels should be optimal (at the correct level) to perform well. If a performer gets too excited or 'pumped up' in a sporting situation, this can result in aggressive acts occurring, for example:

- if a football player is over-aroused, they may launch into a reckless tackle to hurt someone (direct aggression)
- if a rugby player is over-aroused, they may mistime a tackle, deliberately choosing to hit the opponent too high (direct aggression)
- if a tennis player is over-aroused, they may hit the ball so hard out of frustration that the ball lands over the line (indirect aggression)
- if a rower is over-aroused and tries to pull their oar hard, they may lose control of their rowing technique (indirect aggression).

Behaviour of the opposition

The behaviour of the opposition can cause a performer to act aggressively. Examples of this include:

- 'Sledging' in cricket is when some players aim to gain an advantage by making derisory comments about their opponents. This may lead to aggressive retaliation.
- Foul play or aggressive acts from one team or player may cause the other team or player to retaliate.
- Bending the rules can frustrate the opposition. For example, taking a long time to serve in tennis may result in the opponent becoming frustrated and using verbal abuse.
- Unsportsmanlike behaviour, for example refusing to shake hands at the end of a match, can result in some performers losing their temper.

Decisions of officials

When an official makes a decision that a performer does not agree with, this can frustrate the performer and can result in aggressive acts. Examples of this include:

- foul play not being acknowledged or punished by officials
- performers failing to accept that the referee's decision is final

Classroom discussion

In class, discuss who has played in a sporting situation where there was a very high level of pressure to win. Did you manage to stay in control of your behaviour? Did you witness a teammate or opponent losing control of their temper?

- officials appearing to favour one player or team
- officials missing important decisions, for example whether the ball was in or out in tennis.

Although instances of direct physical aggression against officials are very rare in sport, from time to time they do occur. Direct verbal aggression is relatively common in some sports, however, with performers arguing with and abusing officials.

Figure 4.15 Being verbally aggressive towards officials

Theories of aggression

Psychologists have proposed a number of theories to explain the aggressive behaviour of sports performers. In general, these theories tend to focus on aggressive acts either being natural instincts of human behaviour or learned acts which have been copied.

Social learning theory

Social learning theory – discussed in relation to personality on page 124 – can also be used to explain how aggressive behaviour is learned and copied. According to the theory, an observer who sees an aggressor being successful with their aggression may copy this behaviour.

The four stages of Albert Bandura's 1977 observational theory are shown in Table 4.4 and explain how an aggressive act may be copied.

Table 4.4 Observational learning as part of social learning

Stage	Sporting example
Stage 1: Attention	The performer observes another person being aggressive, for example performing a bad tackle in football. They see the aggression being successful and being praised and reinforced. Attention is strongest in young and impressionable performers. They may be in awe of older, more-experienced performers.
Stage 2: Retention	The performer retains the information about the aggressive act. They retain what it looked like and how it was successful, and wonder if they could perform such a bad tackle to also gain praise and reinforcement.
Stage 3: Motor reproduction	The performer establishes whether they have the physical attributes and abilities to copy the aggressive act. For example, are they capable of performing such a bad tackle in their next game?
Stage 4: Motivation	The performer establishes what is motivating them to copy the aggressive act. They may well expect praise from their teammates, coach and spectators, or even from their peers or family. If the motivational aspect is strong enough, they will decide to attempt the aggressive act and commit a bad tackle.

In sports where aggression is seen to be part of the game, such as rugby, performers may well witness aggressive tactics being successful. For example, if the defensive tactics of a team are to tackle very hard and push their opponents back, they may well copy this behaviour, particularly if it is being reinforced with praise.

Trait theory

Trait theory – discussed in relation to personality on page 123 – proposes that personality and behaviour are:

- inherited from parents
- stable throughout life
- enduring, lasting one's whole life.

Trait theory suggests that aggressive acts are natural instincts – in other words, humans have a natural desire to 'fight to survive', to compete. Aggression can be thought of as a natural reflex action that is common to all/most humans. Competitive sport can bring out this natural instinct in a performer.

 Group activity

Divide the class into two groups. One group will argue that aggression is explained by social learning and the other that aggression is a result of natural traits. Prepare to set out your case to your teacher so that they can choose whose argument is strongest.

Stretch activity

1 Search for acts of aggression in sport on YouTube. Decide what reasons you feel caused the aggressive act.

2 Make a poster to display in the classroom that outlines the strength of the arguments for and against social learning being used to explain aggressive behaviour.

Know it!

1. Define what aggression is.
2. Using examples, explain the difference between direct and indirect aggression.
3. State five common reasons why aggressive acts occur in sport.
4. Outline the differences between social learning theory and trait theory in relation to aggressive behaviour.
5. Using recent examples, describe three aggressive acts from different sports and outline how the theories of aggression can be used to explain why they occurred.

Links to other units

You can find further information on this topic in Units R042, R043, R045 and R046.

Read about it

Aggression in sport:

https://believeperform.com/education/aggression-in-sport-2

Positive and negative aggression in sport:

https://drstankovich.com/sports-aggression-whats-good-whats-bad

Theories of aggression:

www.psychologydiscussion.net/social-psychology-2/aggression/top-3-theories-of-aggression/1734

Assessment preparation

Think about the tasks that your teacher may set you to assess your knowledge of aggression. Make sure you:

- know what aggression is
- are clear about what is meant by:
  - direct aggression
  - indirect aggression
  - reasons for aggression
  - theories of aggression.

How will you demonstrate how the main theories of aggression can be linked to a performer's actions in a variety of sports?

Mark scheme

LO3: Know how aggression can affect sports performance		
Mark band 1	Mark band 2	Mark band 3
Identifies **some basic** types of and reasons for aggression.	Identifies a **range** of types of and reasons for aggression.	Identifies a **wide range** of types of and reasons for aggression.
Outlines the main theories of aggression, supported with **some simple** examples.	**Describes** the main theories of aggression in **some detail**, supported with **mostly relevant** examples.	**Comprehensively describes** the main theories of aggression supported with **clear** and **relevant** examples.

LO4 Understand the impact of arousal and anxiety on sports performance

Getting started

Try the following three tasks:
- aim to balance a table tennis ball on your finger
- measure out and mark 20 m; try to kick a ball so that it stops exactly at the 20 m mark
- take a rugby ball and see how far you can kick it.

Once you have completed these tasks, discuss how excited or 'pumped' you had to be to do each task.

Explanations of arousal

Arousal is an energised state that can help or hinder performance. It is defined as a physiological and psychological state of excitement varying from deep sleep to intense excitement. In simple terms, performers perform best when they are at the correct level of arousal. This is known as the **optimal level**. If performers are below this level, they may be under-aroused and not motivated or energised to the do the task properly. Similarly, if they are over-aroused they may miss important information or suffer from poor technique.

Anxiety is a term for a state of worry or nervousness. In a similar fashion to arousal, anxiety must be high enough for us to be bothered to do the task properly, but not so high that it hinders performance. Under-aroused and under-anxious performers may not take a task seriously enough. They may not have the focus, concentration or concern necessary over their performance, so end up underperforming.

Key term

Optimal level (of arousal)
The perfect level of arousal for the task being performed.

Classroom discussion

Share with classmates any occasions in your sporting life where you feel you may have been under- or over-aroused for your performance to be most effective.

Theories of how arousal and anxiety affect performance

There are many theories on how arousal and anxiety affect performance.

Drive theory

Drive theory suggests that as we have more motivation, we have more drive to do well. If we have more drive, we will perform better.

Thus, as arousal and anxiety increase, so does performance. This is known as a linear relationship – as one variable goes up, so does the other.

This increase in performance as a result of arousal is most noticeable in high-level, experienced performers. They have the skills required and can still perform those skills in highly aroused situations. However, low-level performers may find that they get over-aroused quickly, so the theory would appear to have some faults. If a beginner keeps getting more aroused, their performance level is unlikely to keep getting better as they cannot control their actions in such an aroused state.

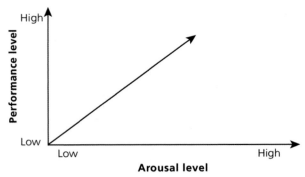

Figure 4.16 Drive theory

Applying drive theory to sporting examples
- If performers are not aroused enough, performance will suffer.
- Elite-level rugby players are able to play in front of big crowds and in highly aroused situations as they have experience and are able to focus and perform well with very high levels of arousal/anxiety.
- Some inexperienced performers may become over-aroused very easily, so the theory appears to have flaws.
- Some elite performers find it hard to get motivated for 'minor' events compared to big international tournaments, so cannot simply become more aroused.

Inverted U theory (Yerkes and Dodson, 1908)

The inverted U theory suggests that there are different optimal levels of arousal; in other words, the correct level of arousal varies from task to task.

The inverted U theory can be summarised in the following way:

- as arousal increases so does performance, up to the optimal point
- if arousal increases further, performance will drop.

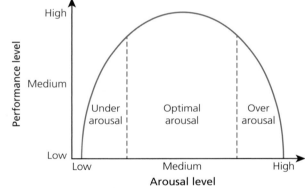

Figure 4.17 The inverted U theory

To experience peak performance, the arousal level must be at the optimal point. It can be seen from Figure 4.17 that under- and over-arousal would cause performance levels to be lower.

Applying the inverted U theory to sporting examples
The inverted U theory can be applied to:

- **Experience level of the performer**: more-experienced performers tend to be able to cope with higher levels of arousal/anxiety. A beginner may struggle to cope with anything higher than a relatively low level of arousal/anxiety.
- **Type of skill being performed**: skills requiring large muscle groups tend to require higher levels of arousal. Skills that require fine, precise movements with few muscles tend to require a lower level of arousal.

For example:

- Sprinting requires a high level of arousal. Elite-level performers can cope with high levels of arousal and are likely to perform well with high levels of arousal/anxiety.
- The triple jump requires large muscle movement. A beginner is likely to lose technique when highly aroused, however, so would function better at a lower arousal level.

These points are reflected in Figure 4.18.

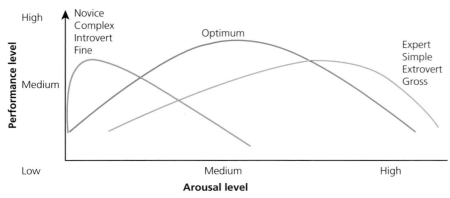

Figure 4.18 Different optimal levels of arousal based on experience and the task being completed

Zone of optimal functioning (Hanin, 1980)

The **zone of optimal functioning** refers to a zone of arousal/anxiety that is optimal for what the performer is doing. This means that the athlete is 'in the zone'; in other words, they are focused, concentrated and suitably aroused to do the task. Some sports require a higher level (zone) of arousal/anxiety than others. Some performers find their appropriate zone at different levels than others.

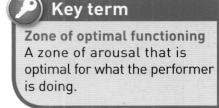

> ### Key term
>
> **Zone of optimal functioning**
> A zone of arousal that is optimal for what the performer is doing.

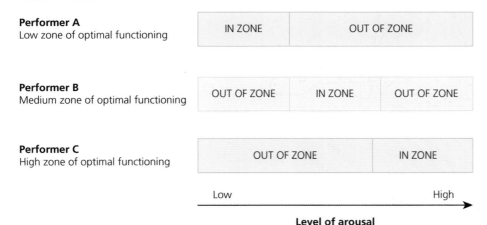

Figure 4.19 Different zones of optimal functioning

In Figure 4.19, the three performers show different zones of optimal functioning, with performer A's being relatively low, performer B being at a medium level and performer C being at a higher arousal level. Most performers have a good idea of where their zone lies. Being below or above their zone of optimal functioning generally results in underperformance.

Applying zones of optimal functioning theory to sporting examples
Some performers put themselves under too much pressure and attempt to work above their zone of optimal functioning. In 1999, golfer Jean van de Velde famously appeared to suffer a bout of over-arousal at the final hole and lost his chance of winning the British Open.

Many performers have techniques that they use to try to remain in their zone of optimal functioning. One example is Cristiano Ronaldo's routine before taking a free kick.

In order to work out their zone of optimal functioning, some athletes use emotional profiling:

1   The performer identifies four to five positive and four to five negative emotions related to successful and unsuccessful performances from the past.

2   The performer then rates how strong or intense those emotions were before and during their successful and unsuccessful performances. They use a ten-point scale (ranging from 'nothing at all' to 'maximal possible').

Figure 4.20 Cristiano Ronaldo using deep breathing to remain in the zone

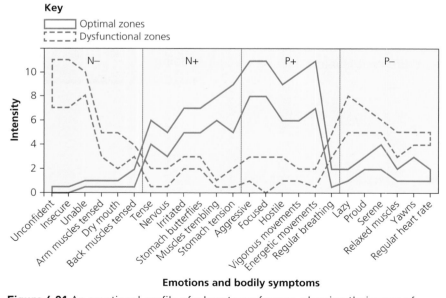

Figure 4.21 An emotional profile of a karate performer, showing their zone of optimal arousal at approximately 50–70 per cent of maximal arousal/anxiety

Methods for measuring anxiety

The two main methods used to measure a performer's anxiety are the:

- sport competition anxiety test, or **SCAT**
- state-trait anxiety inventory test, or **STAI**.

Sport competition anxiety test (SCAT)

A SCAT test involves answering a number of questions about one hour before competition, with answers being 'rarely', 'sometimes' or 'often'. This produces a score, which acts as a measure of the current anxiety level. Although an optimal level of arousal/anxiety is required, based on the results a coach may advise the performer to use techniques to control their anxiety.

Question	Rarely	Sometimes	Often
Competing against others is socially enjoyable	○	○	○
Before I compete, I feel uneasy	○	○	○
Before I compete, I worry about not performing well	○	○	○
I am a good sportsman when I compete	○	○	○
When I compete, I worry about making mistakes	○	○	○
Before I compete, I am calm	○	○	○
Setting a goal is important when competing	○	○	○
Before I compete, I get a queasy feeling in my stomach	○	○	○
Just before competing, I notice my heart beats faster than usual	○	○	○
I like to compete in games that demand a lot of physical energy	○	○	○
Before I compete, I feel relaxed	○	○	○
Before I compete, I am nervous	○	○	○
Team sports are more exciting than individual sports	○	○	○
I get nervous waiting to start the game	○	○	○
Before I compete, I usually get uptight	○	○	○

Figure 4.22 SCAT questions

State-Trait Anxiety Inventory test (STAI)

The state anxiety inventory test is a test of a performer's anxiety. The test (Y-1) has 20 questions that are rated on a scale from one to four. One refers to 'not at all' and four refers to 'very much so'. Go to **http://shodhganga.inflibnet.ac.in/bitstream/10603/40358/1/bibliography%20&%20 appendices.pdf** to see the statements to be assessed. The higher the overall score, the more anxious the performer is.

Group activity

Try out both anxiety tests and compare the overall anxiety score with the rest of the class.

Classroom discussion

Discuss potential positives and negatives about using questionnaires. Are they reliable tests?

Stretch activity

Visit **www.brianmac.co.uk/scat.htm** and attempt the SCAT test. Share your score with a partner. Try to suggest reasons for your score. Can you think of ways that you could reduce your anxiety score?

Know it!

1 State what arousal and anxiety are.
2 Describe drive theory, inverted U theory and zones of optimal functioning.
3 Describe how drive theory, inverted U theory and zones of optimal functioning can be used to explain sporting performance.
4 Describe how SCAT and STAI questionnaires can be used to measure anxiety.

Links to other units

You can find further information on this topic in Units R042, R043, R045 and R046.

Read about it

How sports performers crack under pressure:

www.telegraph.co.uk/sport/football/competitions/premier-league/10484906/Michael-Owen-I-can-see-why-sportsmen-crack-under-pressure.html

Zones of optimal functioning:

https://academy.sportlyzer.com/wiki/arousal-and-performance/individual-zones-of-optimal-functioning-izof

Try the SCAT test:

www.brightredbooks.net/calculators/scat

Assessment preparation

Think about the tasks that your teacher may set you to assess your knowledge of arousal/anxiety. Make sure you:

- know what arousal and anxiety are
- are clear about what is meant by:
  - ○ drive theory
  - ○ inverted U theory
  - ○ zone of optimal functioning theory
  - ○ application of these theories to sporting examples.

How will you demonstrate how you have carried out and interpreted anxiety tests?

Mark scheme

LO4: Understand the impact of arousal and anxiety on sports performance		
Mark band 1	**Mark band 2**	**Mark band 3**
Describes the relationship between arousal and sport performance in **basic** terms. Makes **limited** reference to **some** theories of arousal/anxiety in relation to performance, supported with **few** examples.	**Explains** the relationship between arousal and sport performance in **detail**. Makes reference to **many** of the theories of arousal/anxiety in relation to performance with **some accuracy**, supported with a **range** of examples.	**Explains** the relationship between arousal and sport performance **comprehensively**. Makes **accurate** reference to **all** of the theories of arousal/anxiety in relation to performance, supported with a **wide range** of examples.
Mark band 1	**Mark band 2**	**Mark band 3**
Shows a **limited** ability to carry out anxiety tests.	Able to carry out anxiety tests **competently**.	Able to carry out anxiety tests to a **high standard**.

145

L05 Be able to apply sport psychology strategies to enhance sports performance

The use of goal setting for motivation in sport

Goals should be set for a performer that are **SMART**. This stands for: specific, measurable, achievable, realistic and time-bound. SMART goals help to motivate a performer, as they know that they are actually possible to achieve and can help them to remain focused.

- **S**pecific – the goal should be specific to the performer, their needs and the sport of their choice.
- **M**easurable – the goal should have an element that can be measured.
- **A**chievable – the performer should have the ability to achieve the goal.
- **R**ealistic – the goal should be realistic, that is, within the demands of the performer's life/schedule.
- **T**ime-bound – the goal should be achieved over a set period of time.

Table 4.5 Examples of SMART goals for motivation

Scenario	SMART goal	
100 m sprinter with a personal best of 10.25 s	Goal: improve personal best by 0.2 s by the end of the athletics season **S** goal is specific to the performer and to the event **M** the time can be measured **A** a 0.2 s improvement is achievable for someone who is currently running a fast time **R** the sprinter will be training regularly, so it is realistic to fit this into their schedule **T** the time period is set: 'by the end of the athletics season'	
Football player who scored 20 goals last season	Goal: to score more than 20 goals by the end of the season **S** scoring goals is specific to the performer and to football **M** the number of goals can be measured **A** the player has the ability, having scored 20 goals the season before **R** it is realistic to achieve this by the end of the season **T** the time period is set: 'by the end of the season'	
Tennis player with a 50% success rate for first serves going in	Goal: to increase the number of first serves going in at the next tournament **S** the goal is specific to the player and to tennis **M** the number of serves can be counted/measured **A** as the player manages 50%, they do have the ability to achieve more **R** it is realistic that a slight improvement could be experienced by the next tournament; serving is a natural part of tennis, which will be practised **T** the time period is set: 'at the next tournament'	

The use of mental rehearsal and imagery in sport

Different techniques can be used to allow a performer to focus, to control their arousal and anxiety, and to maximise their performance. Two examples are:

- mental rehearsal
- imagery.

Mental rehearsal is imagery but involves the perfect technique. It is a type of imagery which is a generic term for imagining or picturing something. This allows thoughts to be controlled and focus to be maintained. This can also be classed as **imagery**, where the performer pictures something in their head. Imagery can also include performers imagining themselves in a calm, relaxing place to help them to relax, remain calm and focus on the task being done.

Mental rehearsal may be used in many sporting situations, for example:

- rehearsing how a cricket shot should be played
- rehearsing how a basketball shot should be executed
- rehearsing leaving the blocks in sprinting.

Going through the phases of the performance

This involves the performer using imagery to imagine themselves going through the phases of a skill or performance. One example is a swimmer imagining the phases of a good start:

- the starting position on the blocks
- the dive from the blocks through the air
- the entry to the water and underwater stage.

Visualising positive outcomes

Visualisation of positive outcomes is used a lot in sport. Golfers regularly visualise the ball going into the hole when putting, whereas a badminton player may visualise how a smash will be played to win a point. Visualisation can also be used to picture victory, for example how it will look and feel to win a race in the bobsleigh.

Refocusing

Distractions are common in all sporting activities and may cause a loss of focus and concentration. Therefore performers sometimes need to take steps to refocus and use techniques to concentrate on the task in hand. Examples of when refocusing may be required include:

- Failure – when a sports performer fails, it can be hard to accept and can cause them to lose focus. They may need to put the loss or poor performance behind them and refocus on what they aim to achieve.
- Goals – some performers lose sight of their goals or find their set goals too hard (or too easy). In such circumstances, they may need to refocus and re-evaluate what goals they have set.
- Audience – performers in sports where there is a large or noisy audience may find it hard to concentrate. They may need to refocus at different points in the event and regain control of their actions.

> ### Links to other units
> You will find the information in R041 to be important for safely applying sports psychology strategies.

Figure 4.23 A swimmer may imagine and mentally rehearse the perfect performance of the dive from the blocks

The use of relaxation techniques in sport

Breathing control and regulation

Many performers use **breathing control** as a way to manage arousal and anxiety. Breathing control involves exaggerating breaths in and/or out to regain focus. The body is usually relaxed and the performer tends to breathe slowly to calm nerves and to control arousal. Concentrating on breathing can take the performer's mind off whatever is distracting them.

Releasing tension in muscles

Another relaxation technique involves slowly **releasing tension in muscles**. It is sometimes called **progressive muscular relaxation**. The performer focuses on a part of their body and tenses their muscles. While deep breathing, they then slowly release that tension. This gives the performer a sense of calm and focus. This can be done for a particular muscle or area of the body during performance, or can involve the whole body during a warm up or when training. Many performers start with muscles low in their body and repeat the process moving up their body.

Figure 4.24 Performers on a high diving board often use breathing control to help them focus and remain calm

How to apply appropriate strategies for specific subjects

It is important for a coach or advisor to know what techniques work well for their performer. It is also important for the performer to know the best time to use the techniques. Some examples include:

● A sprinter will be likely to focus before the start of a race, possibly exaggerating breathing and imagining victory.

Key terms

Breathing control Exaggerating breaths in and/or out to regain focus.

Releasing tension in muscles A mixture of deep breathing and the slow release of tense muscles.

Progressive muscular relaxation A mixture of deep breathing and the slow release of tense muscles.

Group activity

Try out some of the relaxation techniques described in this unit. Have a go at breathing control and progressive muscular relaxation.

- A golfer may use mental rehearsal before a shot, imagining how the perfect shot will look.
- A team sports performer may well use exaggerated breathing before a set play, for example before a free kick, a conversion, a penalty flick or a netball free shot or pass.

How to assess whether strategies have had an impact on sports performance

Clearly it is important to evaluate whether the strategies used have had an impact on performance. This can be done in a number of ways:

- **pre- and post-testing** – the performer may complete a SCAT or STAI before and after performance to assess whether their arousal/anxiety level has been reduced
- **basic measures of performance** – the success of strategies may well be evident from basic measures, including for example whether the performer:
  ○ had a higher success rate in passing the ball
  ○ got a better start in the sprint
  ○ managed to control their aggression
  ○ managed to hit more centre points in archery.

These evaluative measures can often be seen simply by observing the performer closely.

 Classroom discussion

Watch the following clip of Cristiano Ronaldo's free kicks:
www.youtube.com/watch?v=N5Dl5jwMf6I

As Ronaldo only scored three free kicks between January 2015 and January 2017, discuss whether his free kick ritual and relaxation techniques actually work or if it is purely 'a show'.

Stretch activity

Produce a leaflet for local athletes to learn about relaxation techniques that they could use and how they might help them.

Know it!

1 State what is meant by the following terms:
  a mental rehearsal
  b imagery
  c visualisation
2 Describe how imagery could be used by a performer in a named sport.
3 Explain how breathing control and progressive muscular relaxation can be used by sports performers.
4 What methods can be used to evaluate how effective psychological strategies have been?

Links to other units

You can find further information on this topic in Units R042, R043, R045 and R046.

Read about it

Visualisation techniques in sport:

www.verywellfit.com/visualization-techniques-for-athletes-3119438

How to set SMART goals:

www.yourcoach.be/en/coaching-tools/smart-goal-setting.php

Assessment preparation

Think about the tasks that your teacher may set you to assess your knowledge of psychological strategies. Make sure you know:

- what SMART goals are
- are clear about what is meant by:
  - mental rehearsal
  - imagery
  - visualisation
  - refocusing
  - the application of these techniques to sporting performers.

How will you demonstrate how you applied these techniques to a performer and evaluated how successful they were?

Mark scheme

LO5: Be able to apply sport psychology strategies to enhance sports performance		
Mark band 1	Mark band 2	Mark band 3
A **limited** range of sport psychology strategies are applied to enhance performance, **few** of which are relevant to the specific needs of the subject(s).	A **range** of sport psychology strategies are applied to enhance performance, **many** of which are relevant to the specific needs of the subject(s).	A **wide range** of sport psychology strategies are applied to enhance performance, **most** of which are relevant to the specific needs of the subject(s).
A **brief** assessment of any impact on the performance of their subject(s) is attempted.	A **detailed** assessment of any impact on the performance of their subject(s) is provided, using **some** different measures and including **relevant** evaluation of aspects of the strategies applied.	A **comprehensive** assessment of any impact on the performance of their subject(s) is provided, **accurately** using **many** different measures and including **relevant** and **insightful** evaluation of the strategies applied.
Little or **no** attempt is made to evaluate the strategies applied.		
Draws on **limited** skills/knowledge/understanding from other units in the specification.	Draws on **some relevant** skills/knowledge/understanding from other units in the specification.	**Clearly** draws on **relevant** skills/knowledge/understanding from other units in the specification.

R045 Sports nutrition

About this chapter

Nutrition and diet are vitally important to our health and well-being. In the world of sport, having the correct nutrition is just as important as having the right equipment and training methods. With unsuitable nutrition, a performer's body would not be able to cope with the stresses and strains put on it. It would lead to a deterioration in performance, and to a deterioration in health.

The need for complex legislation about the use of supplements in elite sport, and the amount of media coverage, highlights the importance of good nutrition in modern-day sport.

In this unit, you will consider the composition of a healthy, balanced diet. You will also consider the necessity of certain nutrients and the effects of a poor diet. You will reflect on the role that diet plays in different sports and activities, and use that knowledge to produce an appropriate, effective diet plan for a performer.

Learning outcomes

LO1 Know about the nutrients needed for a healthy, balanced diet

LO2 Understand the importance of nutrition in sport

LO3 Know about the effects of a poor diet on sports performance and participation

LO4 Be able to develop diet plans for performers

How will I be assessed?

This unit is internally assessed through a written assignment set and marked by your centre; it is worth 25 per cent of the overall mark for the OCR Level 1/2 Cambridge National Certificate in Sport Science. It is estimated that the assignment will take about ten hours to complete and it is worth 60 marks (60 UMS).

OCR provides a model assignment for this unit: http://ocr.org.uk/qualifications/cambridge-nationals/ cambridge-nationals-sport-science-level-1-2-j802-j812/ assessment

For LO1

You need to have knowledge and understanding of:
- the characteristics of a balanced diet
- what nutrients are
- the role of nutrients in a healthy, balanced diet
- food sources of nutrients.

For LO2

You need to have knowledge and understanding of:
- the importance of nutrition before, during and after exercise
- the reasons for the varying dietary requirements of different activity types
- the use of dietary supplements.

For LO3

You need to have knowledge and understanding of:
- malnutrition
- the effects of undereating on sports performance and participation
- the effects of dehydration on sports performance and participation.

For LO4

You need to have knowledge and understanding of:
- how to design a diet plan
- how to evaluate the effectiveness of the diet plan.

LO1 Know about the nutrients needed for a healthy, balanced diet

Characteristics of a balanced diet

A balanced diet is one in which all of the nutrients are obtained in the correct quantities from a range of different foodstuffs. This is important, as no single food contains all the essential nutrients the body needs to stay healthy and work properly.

Therefore, our diets should contain a **variety of different foods**, to help us get the wide range of nutrients that our bodies need. A good starting point is the Eatwell Guide, published by Public Health England. This guide recommends that all adults eat at least five portions of fruit and vegetables a day, two portions of oily fish a week, and that starchy carbohydrates make up around one-third of our daily intake. It also recommends that treats such as chocolate and sweets are eaten in very small amounts.

A healthy, balanced diet should provide us with the right amount of energy from foods and drinks to maintain our **energy balance**. This refers to the balance between the energy taken in from the diet and the amount of energy used by the body.

Getting started

Work in small groups. Each member of the group should write down what they have eaten and drunk in the previous 24 hours. Within the group, discuss whether each person's diet was typical of a 15/16 year old.

We need this energy to carry out everyday tasks such as walking and moving about, but also for all of the functions of the body we may not even think about. Processes such as breathing, pumping blood around the body and thinking also require energy.

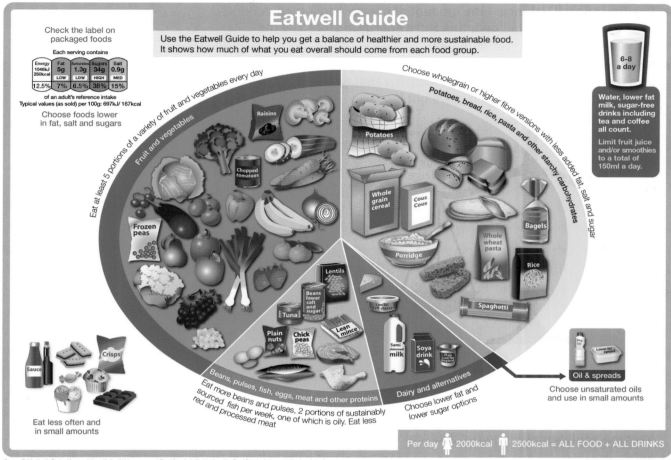

Figure 5.1 The Eatwell Guide

Read about it

What is a balanced diet?

www.healthline.com/health/balanced-diet

The Eatwell Guide:

www.nhs.uk/live-well/eat-well/the-eatwell-guide

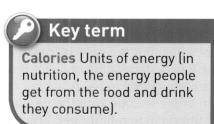

Key term

Calories Units of energy (in nutrition, the energy people get from the food and drink they consume).

Meets the nutritional requirements of an individual

One aspect of a balanced diet means that people are consuming a suitable number of **calories** to meet their nutritional requirements.

Calories are the units of energy. The amount of calories/energy consumed can result in the following outcomes:

- **Energy is balanced** – the amount of energy consumed equals the amount needed.
- **Positive energy balance** – the amount of energy consumed is greater than what is needed; this extra energy is stored by the body as fat, resulting in weight gain.
- **Negative energy balance** – the amount of energy consumed is less than what is needed; the extra energy that we need is taken from our fat stores, resulting in weight loss.

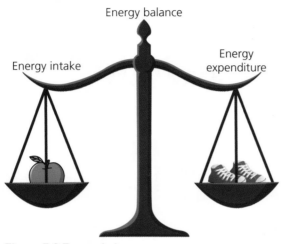

Figure 5.2 Energy balance

The required energy intake depends on several factors:

- gender – men usually need more calories than women; the average adult male requires 2500 calories a day, while the average adult female requires 2000 calories a day
- age – after age 25, the calorie needs of individuals start to fall
- height – taller people tend to require more calories
- energy expenditure – in other words, how much exercise the individual does; the more exercise, the more calories are required
- lifestyle – a job that requires manual labour (such as a builder) will require more energy than a sedentary office job
- **basal metabolic rate (BMR)** – how fast energy is being used

The BMR can vary from individual to individual. It may seem obvious, but the calorie intake required to provide energy for a day will vary depending on what you are doing that day. Some top-class athletes need to eat much more than the average suggested intake in order to cope with the demands of their training schedule e.g. elite cyclists might need around three times as many calories as an average person.

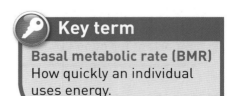

Key term

Basal metabolic rate (BMR)
How quickly an individual uses energy.

So, why should you try to have a balanced diet?

- Suitable amounts of energy should be consumed for the levels of exercise and activity carried out.
- Unused energy is stored as fat, which can cause obesity.
- The human body needs nutrients for energy, growth and hydration.

> **Read about it**
>
> How many calories do you need in a day?
>
> www.healthline.com/nutrition/how-many-calories-per-day#section3

Includes foods from all the food groups

A balanced diet is not only about eating the right number of calories to deal with the energy that will be needed, it is also about eating different food types to provide suitable nutrients.

A balanced diet should include foods from all the food groups: carbohydrates, fats, proteins, fibre, vitamins and minerals, and water.

Contains a variety of foods

Unfortunately, there is no one food that contains all the nutrients the body needs, so it is important that your diet contains a variety of foods. Some foods have particular properties that benefit the body:

- High-fibre cereals and whole grains provide fibre, which prevents constipation and can help to reduce blood cholesterol (fatty deposits).
- Milk, cheese and other dairy products provide calcium, which is good for nerve and muscle function as well as teeth and bone growth.
- Iron-rich foodstuffs, such as liver, help the immune system and assist in the production of red blood cells, which carry oxygen.
- Vitamin A is needed for skin function and growth; it is found in dairy products such as cheese.
- Oily fish, eggs and butter provide vitamin D which is needed by the body to help absorb calcium effectively and is therefore important for good bone health.
- Vitamin C is found in citrus fruit, broccoli and liver; it aids the immune system, skin elasticity and blood vessel function.
- Different types of vitamin B are found in whole grains, nuts, eggs and fish; it assists with various functions of the body.

A truly 'balanced' diet contains lots of different types of food and would normally involve an individual consuming a mixture of carbohydrates, proteins and fats from a variety of sources.

According to the NHS, the ideal mix of different foods should also include green vegetables and fruit to provide the nutrients, vitamins and minerals required. You should aim for at least five portions of fruit and vegetables each day. As a rough guide, one portion is the amount you can fit in the palm of your hand.

The ideal mix of foods is sometimes referred to as the 'seven classes of food': carbohydrate, fat, protein, fibre, vitamins, minerals and water.

Suits the needs/tastes of the individual

We all have food preferences. What some people find tasty, other people find distasteful. Luckily there is a vast array of different foods to suit all needs and tastes.

Some people have a **food allergy**. This is when the body's immune system reacts unusually to specific foods. Although allergic reactions are often mild, they can be very serious and even life-threatening. Symptoms of a food allergy can affect different areas of the body at the same time. Some common symptoms include:

- an itchy sensation inside the mouth, throat or ears
- a raised, itchy red rash – 'hives'
- swelling of the face, around the eyes, lips, tongue and roof of the mouth
- vomiting.

An allergy occurs when your body's natural defences overreact to exposure to a particular substance, treating it as an invader and sending out chemicals to defend against it. While any food can cause an adverse reaction, the following types of food account for about 90 percent of all reactions:

- eggs and milk
- peanuts and nuts from trees
- fish and shellfish
- wheat
- soy
- sesame and mustard seeds.

A **food intolerance** is caused when the digestive system is unable to completely break down food into smaller components. The unabsorbed food becomes a free meal for the bacteria that live in our digestive system. As a result of its consumption by the bacteria, we suffer the classic symptoms of bloating, tummy cramps, wind and, in many cases, diarrhoea.

The most common form of food intolerance is lactose intolerance, which affects more than half the world's population. Luckily this can be treated easily by consuming the required enzymes.

 Key terms

Food allergy A reaction of the immune system to certain foods that it mistakenly perceives as a threat.

Food intolerance Being unable to digest certain types of food.

Food intolerance is completely different from a food allergy, which is caused by an immune response against food proteins. Additionally, food intolerance is not the same as food poisoning, which is caused by toxic substances that would cause symptoms in anyone who ate the food.

> **Read about it**
>
> Food allergies:
>
> www.nhs.uk/conditions/food-allergy
>
> Food intolerance:
>
> www.nhs.uk/conditions/food-intolerance

What are nutrients?

When talking about food, people often use the term **nutrients**. Nutrients are the substances in food that our bodies process to enable them to function. Your nutrient requirements are influenced by factors including your age, growth stage, gender and activity.

Nutrients can generally be split into two categories:

- **macronutrients** – carbohydrates, proteins and fats
- **micronutrients** – vitamins and minerals, such as calcium, iron and vitamin C.

Macronutrients make up most of our diets and provide energy for us to move and function. Micronutrients, on the other hand, are chemical substances that we require in small amounts for healthy growth and development.

Many foods available nowadays are nutrient-poor. This means that they do not contain the nutrition that your body needs to function. Instead, this food is full of excess energy (calories). Nutrient-poor foods include things that are high in sugar and fat, such as refined white bread, pasta, pastries, processed meats and cheeses, ice cream, sweets, fizzy drinks, crisps and chips – in other words, junk food.

This type of food will provide your body with energy (calories), so you will not feel hungry, but it lacks many of the essential nutrients that your body also needs to function.

 Key terms

Macronutrients Nutrients that provide energy, which are needed in the largest amounts in our diet – carbohydrates, proteins and fats.

Micronutrients Nutrients needed in small amounts in our diet that are required for healthy growth and development – vitamins and minerals.

> **Read about it**
>
> Macronutrients:
>
> www.diet.com/g/macronutrients?get=macronutrients
>
> Micronutrients:
>
> www.innerbody.com/nutrition/micronutrients

The role of nutrients in a healthy, balanced diet

Each of the six nutrients has a role in a healthy, balanced diet.

Carbohydrates

Carbohydrates are the main energy source for all types of exercise. The body requires a supply of **glucose** as an energy fuel and carbohydrates are the main source of glucose. The body stores extra glucose as **glycogen** in muscles and in the liver. Thus, for a performer requiring energy, carbohydrates are a very important part of their diet.

Fats

Fats are also an energy source and help to carry vitamins in the body, for example vitamin A. They provide more than double the amount of energy that carbohydrates provide. The key, however, is that fats can only be used as an energy source during low-intensity activity, such as walking and light jogging.

Proteins

Proteins are predominantly used for the growth and repair of body tissues. They also have a small part to play in providing energy. For some performers, particularly those who lift weights and do anaerobic activities, a diet rich in protein is beneficial to help them with the development and repair of muscle tissue.

Fibre

Unlike the other components of a balanced diet, such as fats, proteins and carbohydrates, **fibre** is not digested by your body. Instead, it passes relatively intact through your stomach, small intestine and colon. It helps to prevent constipation and maintain a healthy digestive tract. Foods containing fibre also help to maintain a healthy weight and lower the risk of diabetes and heart disease.

Water

Water consumption is often neglected by people, but it is a vital component of a healthy diet. As water makes up more than half of the human body, it is essential to maintain hydration levels (water balance). Water assists in how the body functions generally. It helps with reactions and lubrication, and also plays a big part in maintaining body temperature. The amount of water you should drink each day depends on several factors:

- the temperature and humidity of the environment you are in – the hotter it is, the more you sweat, and therefore you need more water to replace lost fluids.
- the amount of exercise/activity you are doing – exercising means that you need to replace water (rehydration).

Most guidelines on water intake suggest that we need two to three litres per day.

Vitamins and minerals

Vitamins and minerals are needed for maintaining the efficient working of the body systems and general health. **Vitamins** are organic (carbon-containing) substances that are required for many essential processes in the body; for example, vitamin A is needed for developing the correct structure and function of the skin. **Minerals** are inorganic substances (which do not contain carbon) that assist the body with many of its functions; for example, calcium is needed for bone formation.

> ### Read about it
>
> Nutritional properties:
>
> https://web.archive.org/web/20180808194407/http://www.bbc.co.uk/schools/ gcsebitesize/design/foodtech/compositionpropertiesrev1.shtml
>
> Carbohydrates:
>
> www.healthline.com/health/food-nutrition/ six-essential-nutrients#carbs

Food sources of nutrients

Different foods contain different nutrients. It is important that your diet contains a variety of food sources so that you take in a variety of nutrients, because it usually is not obvious which nutrients are contained in which food.

Sources of carbohydrates

There are many types of carbohydrate (simple and complex) that can be eaten. Sugars, such as sucrose, are simple carbohydrates; simple carbohydrates are also found in fruit, vegetables, honey and milk. Bread, pasta and potatoes provide valuable sources of starch, which is a complex carbohydrate.

Sources of fats

Although fat is a concentrated energy source, it does come in two forms – saturated and unsaturated. Saturated fat usually comes from animal sources such as meat, lard, butter and cheese. Unsaturated fat comes from vegetable sources such as sunflower oil and olive oil. Although many people see fat as an unhealthy part of a diet, you do in fact need to consume 25–30 per cent fat within your normal diet. However, a high fat intake (particularly saturated fat) is strongly linked to many health risks, including:

● high cholesterol levels
● heart disease
● narrowing of the arteries due to fatty deposits.

Figure 5.3 Foods rich in carbohydrates

Good fats   **Bad fats**

Figure 5.4 Some fats are good for you, but many are bad for you

Sources of proteins

The main sources of protein within the diet may come from animal products such as meat, cheese, eggs, fish and dairy products. Vegetable sources of protein include soybean products, pulses, cereals and nuts.

Figure 5.5 Foods rich in protein

Sources of fibre

Fibre, also known as roughage, includes the parts of plant-based foods that your body can not digest or absorb. Fibre is mainly found in fruits, vegetables, whole grains and pulses.

Sources of water

Up to 70 per cent of the water we need is actually found in other drinks such as tea, coffee and juices, and as moisture in the food we eat.

Figure 5.6 Foods rich in fibre

Sources of vitamins and minerals

Our vitamin and mineral intake comes from foods such as fruit and vegetables.

Minerals such as calcium and iron are needed in small amounts to help the body function properly and stay strong:

- **Calcium** is needed for the growth of healthy teeth and bones. Good sources of calcium include milk, cheese, eggs, wholegrain cereals, green vegetables, bread and tofu.
- **Iron** is needed for the formation of red blood cells. Sources of iron include red meat, green vegetables, eggs, lentils and bread.

Other minerals that the body needs include potassium, sodium, magnesium and zinc.

Figure 5.7 Foods rich in vitamins and minerals

Stretch activity

Keep a record of what you eat and drink over a 24-hour period and how much. Analyse your diet by breaking down your recorded intake into separate macro- and micronutrients.

Know it!

1 What are the characteristics of a balanced diet?
2 Describe the sources and roles of four nutrients.

Read about it

NHS advice on eating a balanced diet:

www.nhs.uk/live-well/eat-well/#food-groups-in-our-diet

 ## Classroom discussion

Discuss the results of your findings from the stretch activity with the rest of your class.

Links to other units

You can find further information on this topic in Unit R041.

Assessment preparation

Think about the tasks that your teacher may set you to assess your knowledge of the nutrients needed for a healthy, balanced diet. Make sure you:

- know the characteristics of a balanced diet, i.e. it:
  - meets the nutritional requirements of an individual
  - includes foods from all of the food groups
  - contains a variety of foods
  - suits the needs/tastes of the individual
- know what nutrients are
- know the role of nutrients in a healthy, balanced diet:
  - carbohydrates
  - fats
  - proteins
  - fibre
  - water
  - vitamins and minerals
- know food sources of nutrients:
  - carbohydrates
  - fats
  - proteins
  - fibre
  - water
  - vitamins and minerals.

You will need to include many examples of food sources of nutrients.

Mark scheme

LO1: Know about the nutrients needed for a healthy, balanced diet		
Mark band 1	Mark band 2	Mark band 3
Identifies **some** of the characteristics of a balanced diet.	**Briefly describes most** of the characteristics of a balanced diet.	**Describes in detail all** of the characteristics of a balanced diet.
Provides a **limited** description of what nutrients are and their role within a healthy, balanced diet, giving a **limited** range of examples of food sources of nutrients.	**Describes in detail** what nutrients are and their role within a healthy, balanced diet, giving a **range** of examples of food sources of nutrients.	**Comprehensively describes** what nutrients are and their role within a healthy, balanced diet, giving a **wide range** of examples of food sources of nutrients.

L02 Understand the importance of nutrition in sport

Whether you are a professional performer or simply exercising to improve your health, sports nutrition plays a key role in helping you achieve the full benefits of physical activity. Making better decisions about your nutrition and hydration can not only result in improved performance, but also in better recovery and injury prevention.

Consuming the right balance of food and drink is important for everyone, but those who participate in sport on a regular basis need to be aware that it can also affect their performance. Athletes, for example, will need more calories than the average person because of the extra energy they are using. So, if you are an athlete, or simply someone who has made the decision to start exercising on a regular basis, a good nutrition plan is a priority.

The importance of nutrition before, during and after exercise

As mentioned above, nutrition is important for everybody, but it is especially important for those involved in sport. Good nutrition can make the difference between sporting success and failure. It is essential that performers consider their nutrition before, during and after exercise.

Before exercise

What you eat before exercising will determine how much energy you have during the exercise and how well you perform.

You need to plan your **pre-exercise meal**. The food you eat needs time to be digested, as you do not want to exercise on a full stomach. Normally you should eat three to four hours before you exercise. You should avoid spicy food, which might upset your stomach, and fatty food that takes a long time to digest.

Eat a meal that contains plenty of carbohydrates to increase your blood glucose and stored glycogen levels. The meal should contain a moderate amount of protein to help your body to recover after exercise.

If the plan is for some very strenuous exercise, a small, easily digested snack an hour before might be advised to provide energy quickly.

You might need to experiment with the timings of your meal and/ or snack to make sure that you do not feel uncomfortable once you start exercising.

Getting started

Working with a partner, choose a sport and write a healthy diet plan for a performer in that sport.

Links to other units

You will find the information in R042 to be useful when considering the impact of nutrition.

Key term

Pre-exercise meal Planned food intake three to four hours before exercise.

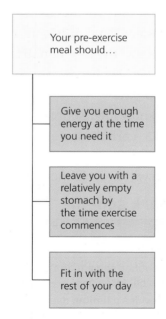

Your pre-exercise meal should…

Give you enough energy at the time you need it

Leave you with a relatively empty stomach by the time exercise commences

Fit in with the rest of your day

Figure 5.8 Pre-exercise meal

During exercise

During moderate- to high-intensity exercise, the body mainly uses carbohydrate for energy, as well as some stored fat. Carbohydrate is found as muscle glycogen and blood glucose in the body.

Many sporting activities can be completed quite adequately if enough focus is put on good general nutrition and the pre-exercise meal. Our carbohydrate (and fat) storage covers most energy needs. It is only if exercise is very intense and long lasting that extra food needs to be consumed. Fluids, however, are an absolute necessity during exercise for the majority of activities, because as the rate of sweating begins to increase, so does the body's need for fluid intake.

Food should only be consumed during exercise if it improves performance. The aim should be to keep blood glucose levels high during prolonged moderate- to high-intensity activities. When glycogen levels start to get low, the body will begin to use blood glucose. Carbohydrates also provide an energy source for the brain during exercise, which will help maintain skill levels and good decision making, and reduce the perception of fatigue.

Lastly, taking in glucose while exercising can spare or help to replenish muscle glycogen. It is thought that any carbohydrate consumed during low-intensity exercise can be used instead, therefore saving or replenishing glycogen stores for later use.

After exercise

You should replace used fluids, carbohydrates and other nutrients immediately after exercise. This is not always possible, however, and eating and drinking may have to fit in with other commitments such as the coach's post-match talk and the cool down.

The main purpose of the recovery is to get you prepared for your next training session or competitive event. The aims are to replace muscle and liver glycogen stores, replace the fluid and salts lost in sweat, and repair the damage caused by the exercise.

The best recovery foods to use are carbohydrates, as these will replace the glycogen depleted during the activity. Recovery will be most effective during the first few hours after the exercise. This is even more important when you have another event in less than eight hours.

Competition venues do not always provide suitable foods and drinks, so plan ahead and bring your own supplies. **Rehydrate** – take on water – as soon as possible after a long workout. Juice, sports drinks and cordial provide carbohydrates as well as fluid for recovery. Carbohydrate snacks that also provide protein may help repair tissue.

If the next session is less than eight hours away, have a snack within 30–60 minutes. An intake of 50–100 g of carbohydrate is adequate to start the refuelling process.

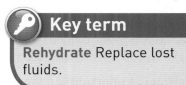

Key term

Rehydrate Replace lost fluids.

Figure 5.9 Rehydration should take place as soon as possible after a long workout

Group activity

Allocate a different sport to each member of the group. Suggest possible dietary intake before, during and after the activity you have been allocated and share your thoughts with the rest of the group.

The reasons for the varying dietary requirements of different activity types

Different types of activity place different demands on the body and, therefore, will have different dietary requirements. This is mainly because different activities use different energy systems.

Endurance/aerobic activities

People involved in **endurance/aerobic activities**, such as marathon running or road cycling, will mainly use aerobic energy. In these types of activities, energy is needed for long periods of time because the event (and the training for the event) may last several hours. Aerobic energy is mainly supplied by carbohydrates.

This type of performer needs a normal, balanced diet, but with some thought being given to the demands of their training and event. To meet the additional energy demands, they may need to increase their carbohydrate intake, so that it makes up 55–70 per cent of their daily diet. They should also be aware of the need for sufficient protein (15 per cent of their daily diet) for the growth and repair of muscles, and take in some iron- and calcium-containing foods.

Hydration is important for the endurance performer. They should drink enough fluids to meet their basic needs as well as replacing the increased fluids used up when training. If training is intense, the addition of carbohydrates and minerals to the fluids may help. One of the current trends is to drink a chocolate milkshake after training, as it contains most of the fluid, carbohydrates, proteins, vitamins and minerals the performer requires.

Vitamins and minerals are very important to the endurance performer, as the training, and the event itself, puts huge demands on the body's ability to work efficiently. Many performers make sure they are eating plenty of fresh fruit and vegetables, as they supply most of the vitamins and minerals they may need.

The body's preferred fuel for any endurance sport is muscle glycogen. If the performer is involved in endurance activities lasting

Key terms

Endurance/aerobic activities Low-intensity, long-duration activities.

Hydration Taking on fluids.

more than two hours, they may use so much muscle glycogen that their glycogen stores become depleted. This results in fatigue and the inability to maintain the duration and intensity of training.

Some endurance athletes manipulate their diet to maximise aerobic energy production. One method is **carbohydrate loading** (often called glycogen- or carbo-loading). Several days before an important competition, the performer eats a diet rich in protein and low in carbohydrates for three days and continues to exercise at relatively high intensity to burn off any existing carbohydrate stores. This is followed by three days of a diet high in carbohydrates and some light training.

The theory is that by completely depleting glycogen stores, they can then be increased by up to two times the original amount and can prevent a performer from suffering from a lack of glycogen during the sporting event.

There are problems with this manipulation, however. Storing extra glycogen makes the performer feel bloated, because it takes extra water to store glycogen. The performer will also be carrying extra weight, which is not beneficial for stamina-based activities. The process is also very much based on trial and error. Performers only find out if it works for them by trying it. There is no guaranteed result. Performers need to guess how many days before competition to begin the high-protein diet, how much to eat, how hard to train, how much carbohydrate to take in when easing off training, and so on.

Key term

Carbohydrate loading
Managing the diet to increase glycogen stores.

Figure 5.10 The energy for aerobic activity is mainly supplied by carbohydrates

Read about it

Nutrition for endurance events:

https://thefoodmedic.co.uk/2017/07/endurance-nutrition

www.topendsports.com/sport/adventure/nutrition.htm

Short, intense/anaerobic activities

In activities such as a middle-distance running race, a 400 m swim or a game of basketball or netball, the performer is involved in short, intense anaerobic activities lasting several minutes with, in the case of basketball and netball, occasional rest periods. The energy demands of this type of activity are different to those needed in endurance/aerobic activities and therefore the dietary requirements are different.

Performers in these activities need to eat a balanced diet containing sufficient calories to meet their energy demands, as they will be using both anaerobic and aerobic energy for the activity. For example, the 400 m swimmer will use anaerobic energy for the intense effort required during the race and aerobic energy during recovery. The netballer will be using anaerobic energy when

Figure 5.11 Performers involved in anaerobic activity have no need to carbo-load, as the event does not last long enough to require it

jumping and sprinting during the game, and aerobic energy during the quieter moments of the game and during recovery.

People involved in these types of activities will need a good supply of carbohydrate as part of their balanced diet, as it is used for both aerobic and anaerobic energy supply. Their diet should contain only a little fat, as fat is only used for energy during periods of inactivity. These performers have no need to carbo-load, as the event (and training) does not last long enough to require it.

Strength-based activities

In strength-based activities, such as weightlifting or shot putting, the performers will mainly be using anaerobic energy. The training sessions involved in these types of activities tend to be very intense and demanding.

To cope with this, their diet needs to contain more calories, based on a higher carbohydrate intake, than a non-performer might need. Similarly, because the activities involve strenuous muscle contractions, the muscles will tend to get bigger (**hypertrophy**), and so extra protein needs to be part of the diet to help build muscle mass. In order to manage their dietary requirements of more calories and more protein, most strength-based performers will eat five to seven meals a day.

Some sports, for example weightlifting and boxing, have different weight categories in which the performers compete. Therefore, it is important that their diet contains relatively little fat, to make sure they do not put on weight. Another reason for having limited fat in their diet is because their training is mainly anaerobic – they do not need energy from fat.

Dietary supplements

For the majority of people involved in exercise, a normal, balanced diet taken through three meals a day should contain sufficient calories and nutrients. However, many sports performers use dietary supplements to obtain all the nutrients they need.

What are dietary supplements?

A dietary supplement is a product that is eaten or drunk and contains one or more ingredients that are intended to supplement a performer's diet. Many performers take dietary supplements containing additional vitamins, minerals, fibre, **fatty acids** or **amino acids** that may be lacking in their diet. Fatty acids are the breakdown products from fat digestion and are needed for a range of processes, including the formation of cell membranes and the correct functioning of the nervous system. Diets that contain little fat may not provide sufficient fatty acids, and so supplements may need to be taken. Amino acids are the breakdown products from

 Key terms

Fatty acids Breakdown products of fats.

Amino acids Breakdown products of proteins.

protein digestion; they are the building blocks from which proteins are made and are needed for building and repairing tissues. Diets that contain little animal protein may not provide sufficient amino acids, and so supplements may need to be taken.

Types of dietary supplements used in sport

There are several types of dietary supplements that performers may take, depending on where they think their own diet may be insufficient.

Like everybody else, a performer's body cannot make vitamins or minerals; they must get them through their diet. This can be achieved by eating a balanced diet containing a variety of fresh food, especially fruit and vegetables. Many sports performers are very busy, however, and may not be able to spend much time shopping, preparing and cooking fresh food. They may need to take **multi-vitamins** to make up for it. These types of supplements are readily available from most high-street chemists and are very popular with performers, as most extra vitamins and minerals can be stored by the body.

Protein powders, available as shakes, bars and capsules, are one of the most popular muscle-building supplements. Protein is an important part of our diet and is key to building and maintaining muscle. It contains amino acids, the building blocks used for muscle growth. Protein supplements are mainly used by performers involved in anaerobic or strength-based activities, who again may not have sufficient time for food preparation.

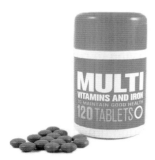

Figure 5.12 Multi-vitamin supplement

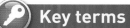

> ## Key terms
>
> **Multi-vitamins** Dietary supplements containing vitamins.
>
> **Protein powders** Dietary supplements containing additional protein.
>
> **Herbal remedies** Dietary supplements derived from plants for medicinal purposes.
>
> **Creatine** Dietary supplements containing creatine phosphate.

Figure 5.13 Protein powders are one of the most popular muscle-building supplements

Herbal remedies – dietary supplements derived from plants for medicinal purposes – are thought to have a beneficial effect for sports people. Herbal remedies have been used for thousands of years, and there are many products available that claim to boost sports performance.

Creatine is found naturally in the body. It is used by muscles to help provide anaerobic energy. Increasing the amount of creatine in the muscles will allow the anaerobic energy system to last longer; it can therefore boost performance in short, intense activities. It can also help improve recovery times. Creatine can be manufactured from plants, meat and fish.

Figure 5.14 Creatine supplements can boost performance in short, intense activities

Why are supplements used in sport?

The reason why supplements are used in sport is that performers are always trying to run faster, jump higher and last longer than the competition.

The use of **multi-vitamins** has more to do with convenience than any direct benefit to performance. The sports performer may simply not have enough time to prepare a suitable range of wholesome fruits, vegetables, whole grains, lean meats and low-fat dairy foods.

Protein powders are readily available to buy in chemists, specialist shops and online. They are taken to help with muscle growth, for weight loss, to reach peak performance, to boost energy and to fight the ageing process.

Although protein shakes are convenient, it should be remembered that the same benefits are available from high-protein foods in the diet. These could be taken as snacks or added to a performer's normal meals to enhance the protein content.

Some **herbal remedies** are thought to reduce lethargy and improve stamina, allowing the performer to train for longer and more often. Ginseng is believed to help increase sports performance by increasing the blood flow around the heart and lungs, allowing for more effective oxygen transfer and therefore improving stamina.

Because many of the substances found in common pain relief medications are banned by the sporting authorities, performers may use herbal remedies for dispersing the pain and discomfort that may occur because of injury or from working muscles too hard while training. For example, many performers use turmeric in the treatment of joint injuries, which may help the athlete to return to training more quickly without the need for prescription drugs, which can have side effects.

Creatine supplements are designed to increase creatine levels in muscles. Performers in explosive events, such as sprinting, jumping and throwing, are likely to experience most benefit, as they can perform at a higher intensity for longer.

Issues associated with the use of supplements

If dietary supplements are so beneficial, why isn't everybody taking them? The most probable reason is that there is a range of issues associated with the use of supplements.

Performers tend to assume that active people need more **vitamins** for better health and performance, but this is not the case. Exercise does not increase your vitamin and mineral requirements. Vitamins are not used as an energy source.

> **Read about it**
>
> Bodybuilding and sports supplements:
>
> www.nhs.uk/live-well/healthy-body/body-building-sports-supplements-facts

Although vitamins and minerals are needed to function efficiently, there is no proof that extra vitamins improve performance, increase strength or endurance, provide energy or build muscle.

Taking a multi-vitamin supplement does not compensate for a high-fat, low-fibre, junk-food diet. If you decide to take a vitamin supplement, look first at your daily diet to see whether you are already consuming these vitamins through highly fortified foods such as breakfast cereals. You can get the recommended amount of most nutrients by eating a variety of foods.

The problem with **protein powders** is, firstly, the expense. Protein is readily available from foods such as chicken, red meat and dairy products, so why waste money on additional protein in a tin? What costs more, a burger or protein powder? Which tastes nicer?

Not all protein shakes are suitable to be used as a meal replacement, because they do not have all the vitamins and nutrients that a balanced meal would contain.

The second problem is that the body cannot store the additional protein. It has to be used to build muscle or the body excretes it in urine. This means that weightlifters who turn to protein supplements, instead of simply eating protein-rich foods, could be wasting their money. A simple change in diet, such as yoghurt with muesli and fruit in the morning rather than plain breakfast cereal and milk, will increase the protein content of a meal.

The problem with **herbal remedies** is that they are not produced under the strictest methods, so people never really know what the remedy contains, and one batch may be very different to another. Some also contain prohibited substances.

Creatine only works if it is used with intense, strength-based, anaerobic exercise. You cannot just take creatine and become stronger or faster. While research has shown that creatine seems to 'modestly' improve strength in adults when taken as a supplement for weight training, and to improve performance in rowing, football and jumping height, there is no conclusive evidence that it can improve sprinting times. Research also suggests that an intake of five grams or more per day usually ends up in urine rather than in the muscle.

There are also possible side effects from taking creatine supplements, including weight gain, dehydration, bloating, muscle cramps and possible liver and kidney damage.

Essentially, the best way to get all the vitamins, minerals and protein needed by those involved in sport is to eat a variety of foods from all the food groups.

 Classroom discussion

Discuss the relative value of different sports performers taking each of the following supplements: multi-vitamins, protein powders, herbal remedies and creatine.

Links to other units

You can find further information on this topic in Units R041, R042, R043 and R046.

Know it!

1 Describe the importance of nutrition before, during and after exercise.

2 Describe the reasons for the varying dietary requirements of endurance, anaerobic and strength-based activities.

3 Describe the different types of dietary supplements used in sport.

Assessment preparation

Think about the tasks that your teacher may set you to assess your knowledge of the importance of nutrition in sport. Make sure you:

● know the importance of nutrition before, during and after exercise
● know the reasons for the varying dietary requirements of different activity types:
  ○ endurance/aerobic activities
  ○ short/intense anaerobic activities
  ○ strength-based activities
● know about the use of dietary supplements:
  ○ definition of dietary supplements
  ○ types of dietary supplements used in sport
  ○ why dietary supplements are used in sport
  ○ issues associated with the use of dietary supplements.

Mark scheme

LO2: The importance of nutrition in sport		
Mark band 1	Mark band 2	Mark band 3
Outlines the importance of nutrition before, during and after exercise.	**Describes** the importance of nutrition before, during and after exercise.	**Explains in detail** the importance of nutrition before, during and after exercise.
Mark band 1	Mark band 2	Mark band 3
Identifies a limited range of different activity types and **outlines basic** dietary requirements for these. Matching of different needs with different activities **lacks accuracy**.	**Identifies a range** of different activity types and **describes basic** dietary requirements for these. Matching of different needs with different activities with some accuracy.	**Identifies a wide range** of different activity types and **explains** dietary requirements for these. **Accurately** matching different needs with different activities.
Mark band 1	Mark band 2	Mark band 3
Briefly describes the use of dietary supplements with **limited** reference to why they are used in sport.	**Describes** the use of dietary supplements with **clear** reference to why they are used in sport.	**Explains** the use of dietary supplements with **detailed** reference to why they are used in sport.
Shows a **limited awareness** of issues associated with their use.	Shows **some understanding** of issues associated with their use.	Shows a **well-developed understanding** of issues associated with their use.

LO3 Know about the effects of a poor diet on sports performance and participation

What is malnutrition?

Malnutrition is a condition that results from an unbalanced diet in which some nutrients are lacking, missing, taken in excess or taken in the wrong proportion.

Malnutrition means 'poor nutrition' and can refer to **undernutrition**, which is not getting enough nutrients, or **overnutrition**, which is getting more nutrients than you need.

Read about it

Malnutrition:

www.nhs.uk/conditions/malnutrition

Vitamin deficiency:

https://en.wikipedia.org/wiki/Vitamin_deficiency

The effects of overeating on sports performance and participation

Overeating is a disorder that affects physical health and causes mental and emotional stress. Overeating affects sports performance and participation because it damages various parts of the body.

Some people tend to eat just because they are bored, or they have nothing else to do. Emotional mood swings – such anger, distress, disappointment or sadness – can make people eat a lot more than they realise.

Some of negative effects of the excessive intake of food include weight gain, obesity, loss of self-confidence and loss of self-esteem. Eating high-calorie junk food often leads to other illnesses such as diabetes.

Deterioration in fitness

It may seem obvious, but carrying excess body fat can affect performance. Being overweight results in fitness deteriorating. Being obese can limit different components of a person's fitness, for example:

- limiting stamina/cardiovascular endurance, making it difficult to perform activities of a long duration
- limiting flexibility, making it difficult for performers to use a full range of movement at joints when attempting to perform skills
- limiting agility, making it difficult to change direction quickly
- limiting speed/power, making it hard to react quickly enough or produce force.

Getting started

Make a list of the effects that could happen from eating a poor diet.

Key terms

Malnutrition Condition that occurs when a person's diet does not contain the right amount of nutrients.

Undernutrition Condition caused by insufficient nutrients in the diet.

Overnutrition Condition caused by excess nutrients in the diet.

Anxiety and loss of confidence

Obesity can also have negative effects on a person's mental health and well-being. Being obese can lead to depression and can cause a loss of confidence. It can lead to an inability to socialise; because the individual is so conscious of how they look, they feel uncomfortable in social situations. This may make the individual feel unable to leave home, so they become anxious and stop or limit participation in sport.

Development of a range of illnesses preventing participation

Obesity can lead to the development of a range of illnesses that may prevent participation. It is a major risk factor for heart disease and heart attacks. It also contributes to an increase in both blood pressure and cholesterol levels. These conditions are all linked as risk factors for heart disease; they will limit participation, as exercise will stress the heart and may need to be avoided (see Unit R043, page 102).

Obesity also leads to the development of diabetes and is linked to the early onset of **arthritis**, especially osteoarthritis. Development of any of these conditions will lead to a reduction in participation because of the pain involved in movement.

Key term

Arthritis Painful inflammation and stiffness of the joints.

Illness during participation

We previously talked about eating before exercise (page 162) and suggested that you should not exercise on a full stomach. Food needs about three to four hours to be digested. If you do eat large amounts of food before a sports activity, it often makes you feel sick during participation. You may well need to stop the activity to prevent being sick.

Read about it

Negative effects of overeating:
www.healthguidance.org/entry/12344/1/Negative-Effects-of-Over-Eating.html

The effects of undereating on sports performance

Eating too little can cause problems for anyone, but making sure that you eat a sufficient number of calories and nutrients is particularly important for sports performers. Performers use more calories than less-active people, and rely more heavily on their muscles, oxygen and energy. Undereating can reduce sports performance and cause potentially serious health risks.

Less energy

We use carbohydrates for energy, mainly in the form of glucose. If you miss meals or do not eat before exercise, your body will struggle to have sufficient glucose available; you will have less energy for your sports performance and will tire much more quickly than you normally do. You will become sluggish, causing you to perform at a lower intensity. The reduced energy supply to your muscles can further detract from your performance and increase your risk of injury.

Weakening of muscles and bones

If you undereat you will have less energy, meaning that you cannot train as hard. You will also be taking in less protein and minerals, notably calcium, and therefore your muscles and bones will gradually weaken over time. Weaker muscles are more prone to strains, while weaker bones are more prone to fractures and joint injuries.

Impaired concentration

In order for your brain to function at its best, you need to have a full complement of nutrients. A lack of nutrients will, therefore, affect brain function and impair your concentration.

Development of eating disorders

Eating disorders are serious mental illnesses that involve disturbed eating behaviour. This might mean: limiting the amount of food eaten; eating very large quantities of food at once (bingeing); getting rid of food eaten through unhealthy means, for example by vomiting or laxative misuse (purging); or a combination of these behaviours.

Anorexia is an eating disorder in which people limit their energy intake, leading to excessive weight loss. It can affect people of any age, gender or background. As well as limiting the amount of food they eat, they may do lots of exercise to burn off the food they have eaten. Some people with anorexia may experience cycles of bingeing and then purging.

Undereating will mean that you lack the nutrients you need for training. Carrying on anyway can lead to **overtraining** and result in injury or illness.

Development of a range of illnesses preventing participation

Undereating or cycles of starvation and bingeing can lead to vitamin deficiencies. Many of these deficiencies can lead to illnesses that prevent you from participating, such as weak bones, reduced levels of haemoglobin (anaemia) and kidney infections.

Key term

Anorexia Eating disorder in which people eat too little.

Classroom discussion

Discuss the problems associated with over- and undereating.

Read about it

Negative effects of undereating:

https://eatingdisorders.com/articles/general/what-are-the-effects-of-under-eating

Eating disorders:

www.nhs.uk/conditions/Eating-disorders

www.beateatingdisorders.org.uk/types

The effects of dehydration on sports performance and participation

Sufficient water consumption is vital to prevent dehydration (an excessive loss of body water). Dehydration limits the normal functioning of the body and our ability to perform and participate in sports.

Overheating

Dehydration has many harmful effects on the body. Body temperature is likely to increase, leading eventually to **heatstroke**. This is a serious medical emergency that occurs when body temperature gets very high. Symptoms include confusion, agitation, the absence of sweating and coma. Heatstroke is treated by cooling the victim, which invariably means contacting the emergency services.

Impaired concentration

Our blood becomes thicker (more **viscous**) when we are dehydrated, which slows down blood flow. This means that less blood gets to the brain and our reaction time increases – in other words, it gets slower and general reactions are poorer. Decision-making is also negatively affected and concentration is impaired, both of which affect performance.

Tiring more quickly

When you are dehydrated, the heart rate increases as it tries to pump the more viscous blood around the body. The body tries to maintain a good blood flow to the brain but, as a consequence of this, blood flow becomes restricted to other parts of the body. This causes individuals to suffer muscle fatigue and muscle cramps so that they tire more quickly, which affects performance.

Illness during participation

Dehydration can also lead to the body trying to conserve water by slowing down bodily functions. This, in turn, can lead to an upset stomach and **vomiting** as you become ill during participation.

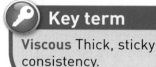

Key term

Viscous Thick, sticky consistency.

> ### Read about it
>
> What is dehydration?
>
> www.webmd.com/a-to-z-guides/dehydration-adults#1
>
> http://news.bbc.co.uk/sport1/hi/health_and_fitness/4289412.stm

Know it!

1   Describe the effects of overeating on sports performance.
2   Describe the effects of undereating on sports performance.
3   Describe the effects of dehydration on sports performance.

Links to other units

You can find further information on this topic in Units R041, R042, R043, R044 and R046.

Assessment preparation

Think about the tasks that your teacher may set you to assess your knowledge of the effects of a poor diet on sports performance and participation. Make sure you:

- know the definition of malnutrition
- know the effects of overeating on sports performance and participation:
  - if you are overweight your fitness will deteriorate
  - you lose confidence and become anxious about participating
  - you can develop a range of illnesses
  - eating large amounts immediately before participating in a sports activity can make you feel sick during participation
- know the effects of undereating on sports performance and participation:
  - you will have less energy
  - your muscles and bones weaken, increasing the risk of injury
  - your concentration becomes impaired
  - you may develop an eating disorder
  - you may develop an illness that prevents you from participating
- know the effects of dehydration on sports performance and participation:
  - you can overheat, leading to heatstroke
  - your concentration becomes impaired
  - you tire more quickly
  - you become ill during participation.

You will need to use relevant information from other units such as R041, R042, R043, R044 and R046.

Mark scheme

LO3: Know about the effects of a poor diet on sports performance and participation		
Mark band 1	Mark band 2	Mark band 3
Definition of malnutrition is **limited**.	Definition of malnutrition is **accurate with some detail**.	Definition of malnutrition is accurate and **detailed**.
Mark band 1	Mark band 2	Mark band 3
Outlines the effects of overeating, undereating and dehydration using **limited** reference to sports performance and participation. Draws on **limited** skills/knowledge/understanding from other units in the specification.	**Describes** the effects of overeating, undereating and dehydration using some clear reference to sports performance and participation. Draws on **some relevant** skills/knowledge/understanding from other units in the specification.	**Explains in detail** the effects of overeating, undereating and dehydration with clear and **specific** reference to sports performance and participation. **Clearly** draws on **relevant** skills/knowledge/understanding from other units in the specification.

L04 Be able to develop diet plans for performers

How to design a diet plan

When designing a diet plan for somebody else, the most important consideration is how to make the plan specific to the individual's needs and what they hope to achieve.

The diet plan must be detailed enough to avoid any confusion about its content and include specific proportions and quantities.

It is no good making suggestions of what to eat if the person you are planning the diet for does not like or cannot afford to buy a particular type of food. Similarly, you need to be fully aware of any allergies, dietary restrictions (for example because of religious beliefs) and cooking abilities.

Finally, and possibly most importantly, you must have a clear understanding of what the performer wants to achieve through the diet plan. Are they hoping to lose weight or gain weight, or are they preparing for a particular event?

Gather details about the performer

In order to plan a diet, you need to gather details about the performer. You need to interview them to find out things such as their age and gender and their food preferences – what foods they like and dislike, or prefer not to eat. You need to know if they have any restrictions because of allergies or their religious beliefs.

Keeping in mind that they are going to have to eat the food listed in this diet plan, you need to know the extent of their cooking skills and the time available for food shopping and preparation. The fresher the foods in the diet plan, the more frequently the performer will have to shop.

You also need to know of any possible limitation on the cost of buying food. Some foods are simply too expensive for some people.

Finally, you need to be aware of the performers's involvement in exercise. What is their chosen sport, how often and for how long do they train, and what activities does their training involve?

Clarify the aims of the diet plan

You need to clarify the aims of the diet plan with the performer. Some performers may want to lose or gain weight. Some performers may wish to manage their diet so that they can train for longer before taking part in a specific event. Others may want to increase their consumption of 'healthy' foods, trying to increase their intake of vitamins or minerals. Others may have specific intentions, such as protein supplementation for a strength-improvement programme, or glycogen loading for an upcoming endurance event.

Set measurable, realistic goals

It is important that realistic goals are set for the diet plan. The goals, like all goals, need to follow the SMART principles:

- **S**pecific – this is possibly the most important aspect of goal-setting. Use the information gained about the performer and their requirements to set goals that are specific to them.
- **M**easurable – the goals need to be measurable, preferably by collecting objective data, for example on how heart rate or breathing has changed since the diet plan started. If the performer is trying to lose (or gain) a certain amount of weight each week, measure this by having a weekly weigh-in. Some aspects could also be measured subjectively. For example, the performer could provide an opinion on how hard they are finding training or how hot they feel during training. You could standardise these opinions by providing a limited range of options, such as having the performer choose one of a number of words to describe how hard they found training on a particular day (easy, moderate, hard, very hard, for example).
- **A**ttainable – the goals need to be within the performer's capabilities.
- **R**ealistic – it is no good setting a goal that is far too difficult to achieve. For example, setting the goal of losing 5 lb per week over the next six months actually means attempting to lose 130 lb, or nine stones.
- **T**ime-bound – the goal needs to be achieved within an agreed period of time. You should have a known finish date for your diet plan, by which time the original aims need to have been achieved.

These goals need to be agreed between yourself and the performer, so that you are both clear on the targets being set. They need to written down and a record kept of the progress that the performer is making.

Consider the time of year

The diet plan must consider the time of year that it covers. Many foods, especially fruit and vegetables, are seasonal – they are likely to be more expensive to buy out of season, or may not be available at all.

The training programme may also be seasonal, with many team games such as football having their heavy aerobic training in the weeks before the season actually starts. Similarly, the performer may be planning for a specific event on a particular date in the year, so the diet plan must consider that.

Specify the duration of the diet plan

As part of the goal-setting aspect of the diet plan, there must be a clear indication of the duration of the plan. In other words, when does the plan have to be completed by? Linked to this is the requirement that the plan must have sufficient time to achieve its goals, but not be so long as to become boring and unsustainable. For example, you may need to have an idea of how long it may take to lose or gain weight. How long does it take before training begins to have an effect on the exercising heart or breathing rate, or how long does it take before muscle or cardiac hypertrophy becomes apparent?

Check the suitability of the diet plan

If the previous guidelines are followed, there should not be any reason why the diet plan is not suitable. The plan must meet the needs of the performer, with appropriate proportions of the various recommended nutrients.

You will need to know how much of one type of food is equivalent to a certain number of calories. Many packaged foods give details of their content in terms of calories, proportion of nutrients, and so on, on the packaging. But it is not all that easy. For example, how many oranges does your performer need to eat to get sufficient vitamin C?

Ensure the organisation of the diet plan

The diet plan must be organised so that the performer knows exactly what to buy, prepare, cook and eat for each meal, and each meal should be scheduled for an appropriate time of the day to fit around the performer's requirements for training, rest, sleep and any other commitments.

Read about it

Setting goals for a healthy eating plan:

www.secondscount.org/healthy-living/healthy-living-detail?cid=14a1b2af-1631-4e88-b456-589ee370c2e8#.W9h79vZ2vlU

Healthy weight loss:

https://health.howstuffworks.com/wellness/diet-fitness/weight-loss/how-healthy-weight-loss-works14.htm

Stretch activity

Work with a partner. Each of you should describe a level of involvement in a physical activity for the following two days (this may be real or imagined). You should then produce a diet plan for your partner that will provide sufficient nutrients and calories for them for the next 48 hours.

How to evaluate the effectiveness of the diet plan

The only way to decide whether the plan is working or has worked is to evaluate its effectiveness. This will involve the collection of data. We have talked about the two types of data previously: **objective** and **subjective**.

Recording the outcomes objectively

Remember that objective data (Unit R043, page 110) is the collection of numbers and measurements. Objective measurements are facts. Any changes to the performer's physiology that can be measured must be recorded and written down. Examples include levels of flexibility at joints, resting and exercising heart and breathing rates and the rate of recovery of heart rate. It also includes data such as a performer's weight, the number of meals eaten and the time of the day when they are eaten.

Recording the outcomes subjectively

Subjective data is about opinions. The performer needs to be asked questions and the responses recorded. Is the performer finding their training easier? Do they think their stamina has improved? Are they finding it hard to stick to the diet plan? Are there any foods in the diet plan that they would like to leave out in future?

Improvement

By collecting both objective and subjective data continually, the diet plan can be adjusted and improved. Adjustments might include increasing the number of meals in a day but reducing the size of the portions, or increasing or decreasing the amount of time between a pre-training meal and the start of training. The diet plan will need to be updated regularly to make sure that it remains suitable.

Know it!

1   Describe how to design a diet plan.
2   Describe how to evaluate a diet plan.

Links to other units

You can find further information on this topic in Units R041, R042, R043, RO44 and R046.

Read about it

Sample diet plans for different sports:

https://www.mealplansite.com/sports

Objective versus subjective data:

www.nrsng.com/objective-vs-subjective-data

Assessment preparation

Think about the tasks that your teacher may set you to assess your ability to develop diet plans for performers. Make sure you:

- know how to design a diet plan:
  - gather details about the performer
  - clarify the aims of the diet plan
  - set realistic goals that can be measured
  - consider the time of year
  - specify the duration of the diet plan
  - check the suitability of the diet plan
  - ensure the organisation of the diet plan
- know how to evaluate the effectiveness of the diet plan:
  - record outcomes objectively and subjectively
  - suggest adjustments and improvements.

You will need to plan this diet as independently as possible.

Mark scheme

LO4: Be able to develop diet plans for performers		
Mark band 1	**Mark band 2**	**Mark band 3**
The plan meets **few** of the specific needs and requirements identified in the aims.	The plan meets **many** of the specific needs and requirements identified in the aims.	The plan meets **all** of the specific needs and requirements identified in the aims.
Needs **some** individual support to design the diet plan.	May need **minimal** individual support to design the diet plan.	The diet plan is designed **independently**.
Mark band 1	**Mark band 2**	**Mark band 3**
Evaluation is **brief**, with **limited** reflection on the design and completion of the diet plan.	Evaluation is **detailed** and reflects on **many** aspects of the design and completion of the diet plan.	Evaluation is **comprehensive** and reflects on most aspects of the design and completion of the diet plan.
Ideas for improvement are **general** rather than specific.	Ideas for improvement are **mostly relevant** and **considered**.	Ideas for improvement are **specific** and **justified**.

R046 Technology in sport

About this unit

In this unit, you will begin to understand how technology is used in sport in innovative ways, with the aim of positively affecting the people making use of it.

Professional sport involves vast sums of money – both in terms of amounts being invested and amounts available for successful performance – so you can start to understand the role that technology plays in attempting to provide performers with a range of advantages.

You will also learn how technology affects coaches, officials and spectators during game play and at other times. You will gain knowledge and understanding about how technology can be deemed to provide both advantages and disadvantages to all involved in sport.

Learning outcomes

L01 Know how technology is used in sport
L02 Understand the positive effects of sports technology
L03 Understand the negative effects of sports technology
L04 Be able to evaluate the impact of technology in sport

How will I be assessed?

This is an optional unit. If selected, you will be assessed over 30 guided learning hours. Approximately ten hours of internal assessment will be worth 60 marks (60 UMS). This unit is centre assessed and OCR moderated.

For LO1

You need to have knowledge and understanding of:

- how technology is used to enhance performance
- how technology is used to enhance game play
- how technology is used to enhance spectatorship.

For LO2

You need to have knowledge and understanding of:

- the positive effects of sports technology for performance
- the positive effects of sports technology for game play

- the positive effects of sports technology for spectators
- other positive effects of sports technology.

For LO3

You need to have knowledge and understanding of:

- the negative effects of sports technology for performance
- the negative effects of sports technology for game play
- the negative effects of sports technology for spectators
- other negative effects of sports technology.

For LO4

You need to have knowledge and understanding of:

- the factors affecting the use of technology in sport
- the impact that technology has had.

LO1 Know how technology is used in sport

Getting started

Have a discussion as to how each member of the class uses technology when playing or watching sport. Remember technology can affect how you perform, what you wear, what your coach uses and how you watch sport.

How technology is used to enhance performance

Technology is simply defined as putting scientific knowledge into practical use to solve problems or invent useful tools. Technological advancements are used to improve performance, help coaches and officials during game play and to enhance the viewing experience of spectators.

Fitness testing

Technology can be used to allow fitness testing to be carried out. Examples of this are shown in Table 6.1.

Key term

Technology Putting scientific knowledge into practical use to solve problems or invent useful tools.

Table 6.1 How technology is used to test fitness levels

Heart rate monitor	Cardiovascular machines in fitness gyms often have integrated heart rate monitors that provide an instant reading of a person's heart rate while exercising; this can help the performer to know if they are working in the correct intensity zone
Body fat monitor	Used to provide an instant score/rating of the percentage of body fat that a performer has
CD player	CD players or some other form of electronic sound system are needed to conduct fitness tests such as the multistage fitness test
Stopwatch	Stopwatches can be used to accurately record times in fitness tests
Fitness tracker	Performers often wear fitness trackers, such as a Fitbit or Apple Watch, to enable them to record the number of steps they have taken, their heart rate and the distance covered
Blood pressure reader	Many gyms can take blood pressure readings to ensure that the performer's blood pressure is within the expected norms; high blood pressure can increase your risk of serious problems such as heart attacks and strokes

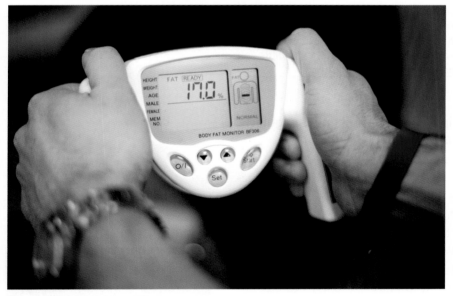

Figure 6.1 A body fat monitor

Training aids

Technology is also used to enhance and aid the training experience of performers. Some examples of this are given in Table 6.2.

Table 6.2 How technology is used to enhance and aid training

Motion tracking software	**Motion tracking software** tracks the movement of a performer and the distance covered Sporting actions can be recorded and slowed down to analyse the technique used; movements can be seen from different angles to work out how technique and performance can be improved When distance and movement are recorded in team games, the coach can decide if the performer is working hard enough and fulfilling their positional role
Simulators	**Simulators** allow you to simulate the real-world action and outcome of a sporting skill in an artificial environment; examples of simulators that are used for training purposes include: ● golf simulators, which allow performers to practise in a controlled, indoor environment; they hit the ball towards a screen, which then shows visually how the ball would travel ● rowing and cycling simulators, which allow performers to carry out the activity in a controlled, indoor environment while providing statistics on speed and visually showing how well they are performing The controlled environment of a simulator allows performers to focus and avoid distractions such as the weather and other people training
Mechanical assistance	**Mechanical assistance** is the use of devices or equipment to guide and support the performer when performing a skill A trampoline harness is a form of mechanical training aid that allows the performer to feel safe and supported while attempting difficult moves such as somersaults; this builds confidence and develops the feeling of doing the move

Key terms

Motion tracking software Technology that tracks the movement of and distance covered by a performer.

Simulators Technology that allows you to simulate the real-world action and outcome of a sporting skill in an artificial environment.

Mechanical assistance The use of devices or equipment to guide and support a performer when performing a skill.

Carbon fibre A composite material with a high strength-to-weight ratio.

Equipment

The design and development of equipment in sport changes regularly as new and innovative technologies are adopted. This includes equipment that a performer throws, holds or even sits in. Some examples are given below:

● Golf clubs have changed with the advent of carbon fibre and graphite shafts, and new technology within the head of the club, allowing the ball to be struck further with greater force and a bigger 'sweet spot' (the point at which the ball is struck).

● Formula One racing cars are redesigned every year in an attempt to make better use of technology and to enable the cars to be more aerodynamic, more fuel-efficient and to move with an increased downwards force to stay on the track at faster speeds.

● Carbon-fibre javelins can assist in producing a more streamlined flight path through the air and can result in the javelin being thrown further. However, javelins were being thrown too far some years ago, so a redesign meant that the centre of gravity was moved forwards 4 cm to help them stick in the ground.

● Bicycles used on the road or in a velodrome are now commonly made with **carbon fibre**, making them lighter and more aerodynamic than ever.

Figure 6.2 Carbon-fibre velodrome bicycles are light and aerodnamic

Clothing and footwear

Clothing and footwear for sports use are designed for purpose, making use of technological advances to improve performance. Examples include:

- lightweight body armour to prevent injuries in rugby
- swimsuits and caps that cause less **drag**
- football boots that improve the bend on a ball
- lightweight running trainers that absorb shock and allow a full, natural running movement
- breathable, waterproof clothing worn by sailors to protect them from the elements, for example Gore-Tex.

Injury prevention and recovery

Technology can be used to prevent injuries and to help performers recover from injuries. Some examples are given below:

- Shin guards and mouth guards protect performers from injury in sports such as hockey.
- Helmets are worn in sports like hockey, American football, cycling and bobsleigh to prevent impact injuries to the head.
- **Hyperbaric chambers** provide a medical treatment that accelerates the body's natural healing process following injury or disease. During hyperbaric oxygen therapy, you breathe pure oxygen inside a highly pressured chamber.

How technology is used to enhance game play

Technology that ensures officials communicate with each other and make the correct decisions can enhance game play. Examples of this are given below:

- **Video refereeing** – television match official (TMO) in rugby allows key decisions to be watched on television by another referee to help the official on the field. Video assistant referees (VARs) are also now used in football and support the system of **goal-line technology**, which shows whether a ball has crossed the line or not. Similarly, the **umpire decision review system** (DRS) in cricket is a technology-based system used to review controversial decisions made by the on-field umpires as to whether or not a batsman had been dismissed.
- **Hawk-Eye** is a system used in tennis to determine if the ball was in or out.
- **Hot spot** is an infrared imaging system used in cricket to determine whether the ball hit the bat or a pad.
- **Radio** – officials in many sports have technology to communicate with each other during the game, for example in rugby.

Group activity

Research the various items of clothing and footwear that are used in different sports. Compare what these items used to be made from with what they are made of now. How has this helped performers in these sports?

Key terms

Drag The resistant force that water exerts against the body.

Hyperbaric chamber Medical treatment in which you breathe pure oxygen inside a highly pressured chamber; it accelerates the body's natural healing process following injury or disease.

Umpire decision review system (DRS) Technology-based system used in cricket to review controversial decisions made by the on-field umpires as to whether or not a batsman had been dismissed.

- **Stadia** – some stadia have retractable roofs so that the weather does not interfere with game play. This is used regularly at Wimbledon to allow play to continue on Centre Court if it rains. Many stadia have under-pitch heating to reduce the potential of cold or icy weather making play unsafe. Some stadia also have the latest generation of artificial pitches e.g. Sutton United in the National League. Tottenham Hotspur's new stadium has a retractable pitch that allows it to change between grass and an artificial pitch.

How technology is used to enhance spectatorship

Spectatorship refers to those watching at the sporting event, on the move or at home. Technological advances have enhanced the experience of spectators in a variety of ways. Examples include:

- **Stadia** – many stadia have big screens to allow spectators to keep up to date with the time and score, and to watch instant replays. Modern stadia are also designed and built without the need for supportive pillars, which used to obstruct the view of spectators.
- **Officials** – in some sports, such as rugby, the referee's decision is broadcast live over the speaker system within the ground, allowing the justification for the decision to be made clear to spectators.
- **Commentary/punditry** – TV pundits now have more information at their disposal to provide informed commentary. Pundits at live sports events and on highlights programmes such as *Match of the Day* can make use of action replays and player tracking (how far people have run or at what speed). Making use of the technology available allows commentators to inform spectators, both during and after play.
- **Television** – HDTV, 3D TV and 4K TV all improve the viewing experience of the spectator. Interactive programmes allow spectators to choose what to watch using a multi-screen feature 'through the red button'.
- **Internet** – the internet provides 24/7 coverage and updates, keeping spectators informed of all news and events relating to their favourite sports. Fans can make use of team/club websites, social networking with players/fans and mobile phone apps while on the move.

Key term

Spectatorship Those watching at the sporting event, on the move or at home.

Classroom discussion

In what ways do you keep up to date with the news and events of your favourite sports and teams? Does anyone in the class access information regularly as part of their day-to-day routine?

Group activity

Design a poster for your favourite sports team to advertise all the ways that fans can keep up to date with news and events at that club.

Stretch activity

Research the success or otherwise of the following methods of video referee, suggesting to others in the group which one has been most successful so far:

- TMO (rugby)
- VAR (football)
- DRS (cricket).

Know it!

1 Define what is meant by the term 'technology'.
2 Describe three different examples of how technology is used to enhance performance.
3 Describe three different examples of how technology is used to enhance game play via officials.
4 Describe three different examples of how technology is used to enhance spectatorship.

Links to other units

You can find further information on this topic in Units R042, R043, R044 and R045.

Read about it

Enhancing stadium technology for the spectator:

https://eandt.theiet.org/content/articles/2017/03/stadium-technology-enhancing-the-spectator-experience

Twenty ways technology makes sports better:

https://bleacherreport.com/articles/773227-20-ways-technology-makes-sports-better

Four ways that technology is enhancing athletic performance:

www.richardvanhooijdonk.com/en/blog/4-ways-technological-innovation-enhances-athletic-performance

Assessment preparation

Think about the tasks that your teacher may set you to assess your knowledge of technology in sport. Make sure you:

- know what technology is
- are clear about examples of:
  - how technology is used to enhance performance
  - how technology is used to enhance game play (via officials)
  - how technology is used to enhance spectatorship.

How will you demonstrate that you have knowledge of a wide range of examples of how technology impacts on performance, game play and spectatorship?

Mark scheme

L01: Know how technology is used in sport		
Mark band 1	Mark band 2	Mark band 3
Outlines the use of technology to enhance performance, game play and spectatorship in sport giving a **limited** range of examples.	**Describes** the use of technology to enhance performance, game play and spectatorship in sport giving a **range** of examples.	**Comprehensively describes** the use of technology to enhance performance, game play and spectatorship in sport giving a **wide range** of examples.

L02 Understand the positive effects of sports technology

The positive effects of sports technology in performance

New technology is generally introduced to cause improvement or enhance efficiency, and this can be seen in many ways within sport.

Equipment is easier to use

One good example is tennis rackets, which are now generally lighter than the old wooden-framed rackets. They make use of a larger hitting spot and carbon-fibre design, which can generate more power. **Carbon fibre** is a composite material with a high strength-to-weight ratio.

Other examples are shown in Figure 6.3.

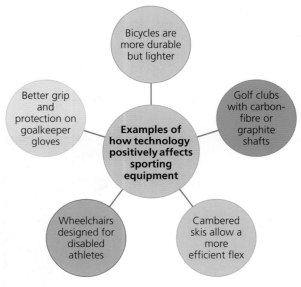

Figure 6.3 Examples of how technology positively affects sporting equipment

Technology can be used to reduce injury

One particular example is the design of footwear, for example for running. Trainers now make use of different types of foam, rubber, gel cushioning and air cushioning to increase durability, comfort, range of movement and support. Many trainers have a **shock zone** to reduce the impact of the foot hitting the ground, limiting the strain on the performer's legs and ankles.

Temperature-regulating clothing helps to prevent overheating and dehydration. The Climacool range of clothing by adidas, for example, suggests that you can experience excellent ventilation while training hard and staying cool.

Key term

Shock zone Area of the foot that impacts with the ground when running.

Links to other units

You will find the information in R041 to be useful when thinking about the imapct of technology on injury prevention.

The materials used in **protective clothing** have evolved to provide lightweight protection for varying body parts. Examples include shin pads in football and hockey, mouth guards in rugby and hockey, helmets in ice hockey and cycling, and body armour in rugby.

Recovery time from injury

Recovery time from injury is reduced when making use of technology, which allows performers to return to training sooner. As mentioned earlier, treatment in hyperbaric chambers helps to reduce swelling, stimulates white blood cell activity and increases the blood supply to the injured site. **Aquatic therapy** in water adjusts the pressure and resistance on an athlete to assist with recovery and rehabilitation. This therapy allows the body to work at a reduced intensity without being placed under normal or potentially damaging stress.

> ### Read about it
>
> How technology is improving sports injury prevention and recovery:
>
> www.industrytap.com/technology-improving-sports-injury-prevention-recovery/38900

Improved training aids

General improvements in training aids help coaches, support employees and performers. This involves all aspects of care and support, both before, during and after training. Coaches can use technology to take baseline physiological measures (for example heart rate and blood pressure) easily prior to training, analyse performance during training, and speed up recovery after training (for example by using ice baths or ultrasound). Specific weaknesses can be identified and targeted, for example adjusting technique to allow for injury. This allows athletes to continue performing until a later age.

The positive effects of sports technology during game play

Technology enhances how the sport is played

Some examples are given below:

- Technology has allowed tennis balls to be hit harder and with more spin, speeding up and intensifying play.
- Cyclists can now cycle faster due to their lighter, more aerodynamic bicycles.
- Footballs are now lighter to head and more prone to spin in the air.
- Para-athletes have lighter, more manoeuvrable wheelchairs, making sports such as wheelchair basketball faster and more intense.
- Athletes with missing limbs can compete with the use of prosthetic limbs or carbon-fibre **blades**, allowing them to run normally and efficiently.

> ### Key terms
>
> **Protective clothing** Clothing designed to prevent injury in sport.
>
> **Aquatic therapy** Fluid environment that adjusts the pressure and resistance on an athlete to assist with recovery and rehabilitation.

Figure 6.4 Hyperbaric chamber

Figure 6.5 Aquatic therapy pool

> ### Key term
>
> **Blade** Artificial part of a limb made from carbon fibre.

Read about it

Blade running:

www.paralympic.org/news/para-athletics-explained-blade-running

Technology increases competition

Performers can watch highlights programmes in which experts analyse the performance of a person or team. Subsequently, tactics can be planned to counteract an opponent's strengths and exploit their weaknesses. Equally, a personal performance can be analysed using video footage and software – performers can plan to maximise their own strengths and apply strategies that allow them to use their skills most effectively.

Technology improves accuracy

Decisions made by officials are more accurate when technology is used. Examples in athletics include how throwing and jumping events are measured using laser measuring, and how timing is recorded and displayed during track events. Officials are able to make more accurate decisions by using video replays. This makes the sporting event fairer for all competitors, as fewer wrong decisions are made. Examples include:

- TMO in rugby
- VAR in football
- DRS in cricket
- Hawk-Eye in tennis.

Read about it

How VAR was used at the World Cup 2018:

www.telegraph.co.uk/world-cup/0/var-rules-used-fifa-world-cup-2018-russia

The positive effects of sports technology on spectatorship

Technology can increase the fan base

Technology can increase the fan base of a sport or sporting club by making information more accessible and exciting. Fans can keep up to date with statistics, news and events at their favourite club or in their favourite sport in a variety of ways, as shown in Figure 6.6. Tickets for sports fixtures can also be bought online easily.

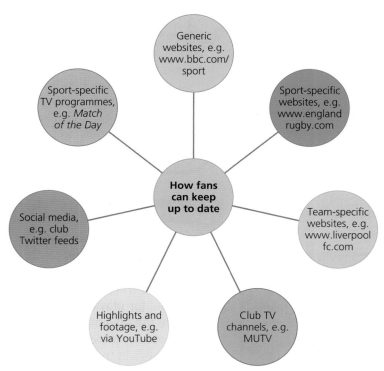

Figure 6.6 How fans can keep up to date

Technology allows spectators to see all the action

Technology can be used to show spectators instant replays. Slow-motion replays and multiple camera angles can be used to provide a complete and informed view of the action. One example is seeing athletes hitting the take-off board in the triple or long jump in a close-up and slow-motion replay. Such technology can also allow viewers to see rugby performances from above the centre of the pitch using a 'pitch cam'. Sports events can be seen in closer detail, with viewers able to rewind and replay footage via their televisions, smart phones or tablets. In simple terms, viewers are now able to ensure that they do not miss any of the action.

Other positive effects of sports technology

Technology affects all aspects of sport, for performers, coaches, officials and spectators. However, the impact of technological developments is not only seen by elite-level, professional sports performers. Technological developments filter down to recreational performers and the public in general, who benefit from developments in equipment, clothing, footwear and analysis tools.

Sports technology can provide health care benefits to a wider audience. For instance, prosthetic limbs and blades that were originally developed for sport are now available to ordinary people to help them live their lives more comfortably. In addition, amateur disabled athletes can take part in sporting activities while making use of specialised and adapted equipment. Wheelchairs are generally now lighter and easier to manoeuvre.

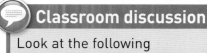

Classroom discussion

Look at the following websites. Debate and discuss which site is more informative and engaging for sports fans:

● www.bbc.com/sport
● www.skysports.com

Sports technology can reach a wider and more general audience in other ways too. For instance, road cars available for public sale are increasingly made from carbon fibre that was originally pioneered in Formula One racing cars. Equally, carbon-fibre road bicycles have become more accessible and affordable for amateur cyclists.

Major sports companies provide affordable equipment that uses some of the same technologies used by elite performers. High-street chains sell trainers that make use of specialist technology to increase comfort and support for amateur runners. Carbon-fibre and graphite golf clubs are now commonplace at public golf clubs. Amateur hockey performers can wear face masks, made from a high-impact-resistant polycarbonate shell and dual-density foam padding, to protect them during corners.

Stretch activity

1 Design a piece of sporting equipment or clothing that does not currently exist. State what benefits your design will bring performers in the sport that it would be used in.

2 Write an overview of all the technology that a sporting performer of your choice makes use of. Think about training, rehabilitation, clothing, equipment, footwear, coaching, analysis and so on. Present your findings with pictures to the group.

Know it!

1 State a range of technological developments in different equipment used in sport.

2 Describe how technology is used by coaches to analyse performance.

3 Name and describe three different examples of technological developments that prevent or speed up recovery from injury.

4 Identify three different examples of how officials can make use of technological developments during game play.

5 Describe the benefits that technological developments provide spectators when attending a sporting event or watching at home.

6 State two examples of technological developments in sports that are now commonly used by amateur performers in that sport.

Classroom discussion

Which sports performers do you feel have made the best use of technology for their benefit? How have they used that technology to increase the level of their performance?

Group activity

Design a poster advertising your favourite sporting footwear product, for example a trainer for running or a boot for playing football. Include the advantages that this footwear provides for performers in that sporting activity.

Links to other units

You can find further information on this topic in Units R042, R043, R044 and R045.

Read about it

Wheelchair technology in sport:

https://theconversation.com/wheelchair-technology-in-the-paralympics-and-its-spin-offs-8924

How archer's bows have improved:

www.deeranddeerhunting.com/articles/deer-news/high-tech-innovations-have-improved-traditional-archery-performance

Assessment preparation

Think about the tasks that your teacher may set you to assess your knowledge of the positive effects of sports technology. Make sure you:

- know a range of examples of equipment used in sport for positive reasons
- are clear about a range of examples of technology used:
  - to prevent or treat injuries
  - during game play to assist officials
  - to enhance the experience of spectators.

How will you demonstrate how technology is used positively in sport?

Mark scheme

LO2: Understand the positive effects of sports technology		
Mark band 1	Mark band 2	Mark band 3
Identifies some possible positive effects of sports technology. Provides a **brief description** of the positive effects identified and supports **some** of the descriptions with examples. Draws on **limited** skills/knowledge/understanding from other units in the specification.	**Describes** a **range** of possible positive effects of sports technology. Provides **some explanation** as to why they are positive, supported with **mostly relevant** examples. Draws on **some relevant** skills/knowledge/understanding from other units in the specification.	**Explains** a **wide range** of possible positive effects of sports technology, **clearly** supported with **relevant** examples. **Clearly** draws on relevant skills/knowledge/understanding from other units in the specification.

LO3 Understand the negative effects of sports technology

Although technology in sport is largely seen as providing benefits to those involved, it can also be argued that there are some negative effects. These can be seen or experienced by performers, officials during game play and in other ways.

The negative effects of sports technology in performance

Technological developments in sport can be seen to have a number of negative effects on performers. Examples are given below:

- **Skills may deteriorate** due to an **over-reliance on technology**. In other words, the performer relies on the technology to make up for their lack of skill. As sporting equipment becomes more accurate, effective and forgiving on the performer, it can be argued that the skill level required is reduced. Performers who used old-fashioned wooden tennis rackets had to use a high level of skill to control the ball. Modern carbon-fibre rackets are stronger, provide more string tension and make it much easier to use spin. The need for skilled control is arguably less than in the past.

  Similarly, modern golf clubs with carbon-fibre or graphite shafts and a larger 'sweet spot' to hit the ball are more forgiving on the performer. The golfer can arguably swing and strike the ball with less skill and still manage to strike it relatively accurately. This is particularly the case with hybrid and hollow-bodied irons. Shots are simply easier to hit with a comfortably slow swing. Hollow-bodied irons appeal to many players because their faces flex more efficiently at impact than a traditional iron. This removes some element of skill for the golfer, who can now keep the ball low and below the wind easily. Hitting a golf shot in a manner that keeps the ball below the wind required a lot of skill prior to technological changes.

- Technology can result in **rule or regulation changes**, which move away from the traditions of the sport. This can be deemed negative by those who valued the rules as they were. The introduction of the Hawk-Eye system in tennis has caused a rule change, with players now being allowed to **challenge decisions** made three times per set. If their challenge is correct, they do not lose a challenge. They also receive an extra challenge in a tiebreak.

  Certain swimsuit designs have been banned because of the amount of reduction in drag they provided to elite swimmers. Drag is the resistant force that water exerts against the body. This can provide an unfair advantage for those who can access the most efficient clothing.

Key terms

Over-reliance on technology When performers rely on technology to make up for their lack of skill.

Challenge decisions Decisions in sport that can be challenged as part of the rules or regulations.

Figure 6.7 Are some golf clubs simply making the game too easy?

The umpire decision review system (DRS) in cricket allows cricket captains to choose to review decisions. The number of reviews varies in different formats of cricket. This change has moved away from the traditions of the sport.

Motorsport rules have changed frequently over the years to restrict the degree to which technological advances can be used by competing teams to gain an unfair advantage over the other cars, as the sport would become predictable and somewhat boring.

Read about it

Is technology posing a threat to how fair sport is?

http://theconversation.com/why-technology-in-sport-poses-a-threat-to-keeping-the-game-fair-safe-and-affordable-44475

The negative effects of sports technology in game play

Technology can **prolong the duration of a game**. The need to review or assess decisions in sports such as tennis, cricket, football or rugby has changed the traditional nature of the sport. These decisions take time and mean that the game is prolonged as referees and umpires review the computer-based footage. In some people's opinion, these breaks in play have interrupted the flow of the sport and can make the event feel slightly 'stale'. Traditionalists enjoyed the uninterrupted nature of such sporting events, although others like the extra drama of the reviews.

Figure 6.9 Referee taking time to review footage of a football match, interrupting play; on average, a VAR decision in football takes approximately 68 seconds

Figure 6.8 Cricketer calling for a review

Group activity

Research rules that have changed in a sport of your choice as a result of new technology. Discuss with a partner if these rule changes have benefited or negatively changed the nature of the sport.

Group activity

Watch the following clip on how Hawk-Eye works in tennis:

www.youtube.com/watch?v=XhQyVnwBXBs

Classroom discussion

With reference to a decision-based system in a sport of your choice (for example VAR in football or Hawk-Eye in tennis), discuss the viewpoint that 'technology has negatively affected the traditional nature of the sport'. Prepare your argument for or against the statement.

Technology can **detract from the ethics of sport**. In other words, it can be argued that the winner is now not always the best athlete or performer but the one with the best equipment and technology available to them. The term **technology doping** is now commonly used to describe the practice of gaining competitive advantage by using high-tech sports equipment.

Some examples are given below:

- Team GB's successes at cycling in recent Olympics are commonly attributed in part to the incredible design of the team's bicycles and the aerodynamic bodysuits worn by the athletes.
- Team USA partnered with car giant BMW to redesign all of their sliding equipment for the Winter Olympics, for example their bobsleighs, speed skates and skeleton bobs.
- Team USA teamed up with Under Armour and Lockheed Martin (an aerospace company) in an attempt to design speed-skating suits that would provide an advantage over other competitors at the Winter Olympics.
- Advances in the technology used within Formula One cars may provide an unfair advantage for some drivers over others.

Read about it

How technology provided an advantage at the London 2012 Olympics:

www.theguardian.com/sport/2012/jul/04/london-2012-olympic-games-sport-technology

Key terms

Technology doping
The practice of gaining competitive advantage by using high-tech sports equipment.

Analytical technology
Technology that allows performance and/or physiological measures within the body to be recorded and evaluated.

Classroom discussion

It has been argued that 'winning is less and less about performance and skill but more and more about technology available'. Split the class into two groups. One group should prepare their argument in support of the statement and one against.

The **cost of technology can determine who is able to access and use it**. In other words, only those who can afford it can use it. This can create a gulf between those who can and those who cannot afford the development in technology. This generally relates to equipment but can also relate to clothing and footwear, the cost of coaching and training, and **analytical technology**. Analytical technology is technology that allows performance and/or physiological measures within the body to be recorded and evaluated.

Although rules about velodrome cycling technology have been tightened up, the cost of Team GB's velodrome kit is clearly not affordable for all teams at the Olympic Games. These general costs are given in Table 6.3.

Table 6.3 General costs of a Team GB velodrome cyclist's kit in 2016

Kit	Approximate cost	Description
Helmet	£3,000	The cost included 'honeycomb aluminium technology' for added strength and safety; the helmets were only useful for one crash or collision, however
Handlebars	£5,000	Each set of handlebars was individually made to suit each cyclist; they were generally made of carbon fibre to be lightweight and strong
Skinsuit	£5,000	The skinsuits included triangular strips on the arms that were designed to help air to stick to the body so that there was less air resistance; the suit could only be worn once
Frame	£9,000	The bikes had more carbon around the bottom bracket (where the pedals enter the frame) to stop the riders from snapping off their pedals due to the potential force that they could create through the legs and feet
Wheels	£2,000 each	Most wheels used by the British team featured carbon-fibre spokes for better handling

Read about it

Technology in sport: competitive edge or unfair advantage?

www.pddinnovation.com/technology-sport-competitive-edge-unfair-advantage

The negative effects of sports technology on spectatorship

Technology can also have a negative effect on spectatorship. The positive of being able to access high-quality images of sporting events, from different angles and with instant analysis, can actually result in fewer people attending the event live. As more spectators choose to watch from the comfort of home, without the need to worry about the weather or travel arrangements, the atmosphere in the stadium itself is negatively impacted.

The BBC produced a study in August 2018 which concluded that 11 of the 20 Premier League football clubs no longer needed supporters to attend matches in order to make a profit. This is largely due to money received from television companies rather than because spectators choose not to attend.

Read about it

BBC report into the need for spectators in the Premier League:

www.bbc.co.uk/sport/football/44850888

Other negative effects of sports technology

Technology can damage the **traditional nature of the sport** if the sport has to change in order to accommodate the technology. This is particularly the case with sports that have allowed some form of video review system, for example cricket, rugby, football

Group activity

Design a promotional poster for a sporting event with the intention of accentuating the positives of attending as opposed to watching at home.

Key term

Traditional nature of sport
The standard ways and rules that have been used in a sport for a number of years.

197

and tennis. These sports simply used to involve the referee/ umpire making decisions before the match moved on. Purists do not like the time that review systems add to the game, changing the traditional, uninterrupted version of the sport that they have watched for years.

Although VAR was used extensively in the 2018 World Cup, the Premier League voted against introducing it for the 2018/19 season, but trials are ongoing. VAR was first used to make a crucial decision in English football in the 2018 FA Cup, when Kelechi Iheanacho's goal for Leicester City was given after a review. The goal had initially been ruled offside.

Stretch activity

1 Create a speech to give in support of banning any further technology in sport. Prepare an argument that focuses on the fact that it is damaging to change the traditional nature of sport.

2 If possible, try out an old and a new technologically developed piece of sporting equipment, for example a cricket bat, tennis racket, golf club or bicycle. Discuss with a partner what difference the new technology made and whether it takes away from the need to rely on a level of skill.

Know it!

1 State three uses of technology in sport.

2 Describe three examples of how technology can be deemed to be negative for performers.

3 Describe three examples of how technology can be deemed to be negative in game play.

4 Describe three examples of how technology can be deemed to be negative for spectators.

5 Provide two examples of how the 'traditional nature of sport' has been altered as a result of technological developments.

Read about it

Technology in sport: positive or negative?
www.solveyourtech.com/technology-sport-positive-negative

Classroom discussion

What additional technological advances do you feel could be introduced to help officials make the correct decisions? Do you feel that these changes could interrupt the traditional nature of that sport, so much so that it may be better to simply keep what currently exists?

Figure 6.10 VAR in football has proven to be extremely controversial, changing the nature of the game

Links to other units

You can find further information on this topic in Units R042, R043, R044 and R045.

Assessment preparation

Think about the tasks that your teacher may set you to assess your knowledge of the negative effects of technology in sport. Make sure you:

- know a range of ways in which performers are negatively affected by technology
- are clear about a range of examples that:
  - show how game play has been negatively affected by technology
  - show how decision making during games has been negatively affected by technology
  - show how the traditional nature of sport has been negatively affected by technology
  - show how technology has negatively affected sport in other ways.

How will you demonstrate how technology is negatively affecting those involved in sport using a wide range of examples?

Mark scheme

LO3: Understand the negative effects of sports technology		
Mark band 1	Mark band 2	Mark band 3
Identifies some possible negative effects of sports technology. Provides a **brief description** of the negative effects identified and supports **some** of the descriptions with examples.	**Describes** a **range** of possible negative effects of sports technology. Provides **some explanation** as to why they are negative, supported with **mostly relevant** examples.	**Explains** a **wide range** of possible negative effects of sports technology, **clearly** supported with **relevant** examples.

LO4 Be able to evaluate the impact of technology in sport

Factors affecting the use of technology in sport

It is important to look at ways to evaluate the success and impact of a specific technology in sport. This section discusses the factors that should be considered when making a judgement about the effectiveness of a particular development.

The application of the technological development

Application refers to how the technology is actually put into use – that is, is the technological development actually useful in the way that it is implemented? Can it be used in one sport or many sports? Is there an organisation or sport that is at the forefront of using the technology?

VAR

VAR was initially part of a rather ambitious project by the Royal Netherlands Football Association (KNVB) who launched a project called Refereeing 2.0. With the advent of the internet, it was felt that the referee was the only person in the stadium who could not see a replay of some kind. One of the initial successes was the introduction of goal-line technology by FIFA in 2012, after two years of trialling the product in Holland. However, it was only in October 2015 that FIFA's new boss Gianni Infantino showed a desire to bring the technology into widespread use in football.

Its application has been fraught with difficulties, including the time it takes to make decisions (the average VAR decision takes 68 seconds), how it changes the nature of the game and inconsistencies in its use. Examples include:

- The A-League grand final in Australia between Melbourne Victory and the Newcastle Jets saw the referee try to use VAR after a winning goal was scored from an offside position, but the cameras appeared to have frozen just before the goal.
- In Portugal, one decision could not be made due to a flag that had blown in front of the camera.

On the whole, however, VAR has proven to be a success in football when used to check key decisions such as penalties or goals. It was used extensively in the 2018 World Cup, where many correct decisions were made thanks to the use of VAR.

VAR's application involves five officials in total: the on-pitch referee, the two on-pitch assistants, the fourth official and the video assistant referee (VAR). All five are in constant communication via a headset. After a potentially controversial incident, VAR can make a recommendation to the on-field referee or their opinion can be requested. Video playbacks of an incident are watched by the referee at the side of the pitch.

The reasons for the introduction of the technological development

Most new forms of technology aim to benefit someone. In trying to evaluate their success, however, it is vital to look at the reasons why they were introduced, with particular reference to their impact on performers, game play and spectators.

Reasons for performers

The carbon-fibre bicycle developed for Great Britain Cycling Team track cyclists was certainly introduced with performers in mind and has helped the riders to break records.

Former British Cycling performance director Sir Dave Brailsford led the way in aiming for what he described as **marginal gains**. He believed that marginal gains (small, incremental improvements in any process) would add up to cycling success, including the advent of a ground-breaking bike. Under Brailsford, British cyclist Chris Boardman initially headed up the 'Secret Squirrel Club', a group looking at finding marginal gains across the board.

Their research and development department has worked with aerodynamics experts from BAE Systems and Formula One, regularly using a wind tunnel close to Southampton to look for further marginal gains.

The T5GB bike was developed by Cervélo for Great Britain Cycling Team cyclists ahead of the 2016 Olympic Games.

Figure 6.11 The Cervélo T5GB bike used by Great Britain Cycling Team cyclists

Reasons for game play

It could be said that VAR was developed because football was losing credibility due to the poor decision making of referees. Two distinctive examples of poor decision making are given below:

- Thierry Henry's handball helped France beat Ireland to a place in the 2010 World Cup.

Classroom discussion

As a class, watch the following clip and discuss your thoughts:

www.youtube.com/watch?v=hHUzyJx3rUQ

Key term

Marginal gains Small, incremental improvements in any process.

Read about it

More on the Cervélo bikes used by Great Britain Cycling Team at the World Championships in 2018:

www.cyclingweekly.com/news/british-track-team-debut-brand-new-cervelo-370996

- Frank Lampard's goal for England against Germany in 2014 was not awarded, despite being considerably over the line.

In its design, VAR was intended to eradicate poor decision making during game play.

Reasons for spectators

TMO in rugby gives spectators (whether present at the event or watching at home) the opportunity to watch footage of the decision being judged. This allows spectators to feel involved in the event and to be fully informed as to why decisions are made. Hawk-Eye technology in tennis also allows spectators to see a **visual representation** of the decision being judged.

Table 6.4 Positives and negatives for spectators seeing Hawk-Eye decisions in tennis

Positives	Negatives
Feel part of the event	Disrupts the event
Creates excitement	Not traditional
Visual understanding of decision	Games may take longer
Adds to simply hearing decisions	

Does the technology have any relevance to or detrimental impact on history/tradition?

Many sports have a proud history and those who watch the sport may have a traditional viewpoint of how that sport should be played and officiated. Cricket has a long and illustrious history of performers playing in white and umpires making decisions from a standing point at the end of the wicket. It can be argued that these traditions have been somewhat tainted by the umpire decision review system (DRS). Teams can opt to query a decision, and the umpires can be proven right or wrong by using the system.

Sometimes organisations may be resistant to change, favouring to stick to the traditional ways. As a president of FIFA, Sepp Blatter was notoriously opposed to using the VAR system.

Reactions of key stakeholders

One way to evaluate the success or otherwise of a form of technological development is to ascertain the reactions of **stakeholders**. In sport, these are deemed to be athletes/performers, spectators and professional bodies.

For a technological development such as running blades for disabled athletes, the reactions of stakeholders in sport are rather varied. There are clearly advantages and disadvantages for each stakeholder, which are outlined in Table 6.5.

Key terms

Visual representation
A method to visually show the sporting decision being analysed.

Stakeholders (in sport)
Athletes/performers, spectators and professional bodies.

Figure 6.12 Spectators watching a Hawk-Eye decision at Wimbledon

Figure 6.13 The DRS being used in cricket

Table 6.5 Advantages and disadvantages of running blades for disabled athletes by stakeholder

Stakeholder	Advantages	Disadvantages
Performers	Disabled athletes can compete with a natural running action Potential to show athletic prowess against able-bodied athletes	Have to prove that their blades provide no advantage over able-bodied athletes Can be deemed by many to be using technology to 'cheat'
Spectators	Excitement of seeing technology in action Potential to see able-bodied and disabled athletes competing (potentially against each other)	Some may view the blades as a method of cheating Do not get to see all athletes with blades as some cannot prove that their blades are not providing a competitive advantage
Professional bodies	Can be seen to be inclusive and supportive of disabled athletes Can run able-bodied/para-athlete and mixed events	Require disabled athletes to prove that their blades provide no advantage May appear to be being harsh on some disabled athletes

The introduction of TMO was welcomed by most rugby players, spectators and professional bodies, as it allowed decisions to be fairer for all involved.

However, long-handled anchor putters in golf were eventually banned as many stakeholders felt they gave an unfair advantage to those using them.

Features of technology that affect its use

In evaluating the impact that technology has had in sport, it is perhaps important to look at some of the features that affect its use. Many of these are shown in Figure 6.15.

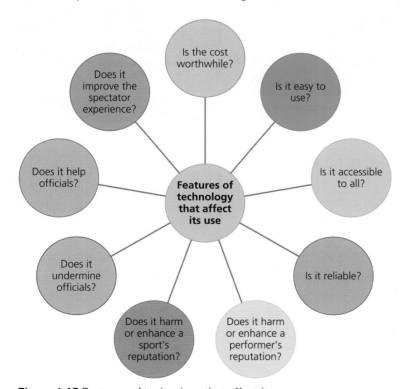

Figure 6.15 Features of technology that affect its use

> **Read about it**
>
> More on the development of blades for **amputee** athletes and how they broke down barriers for this group of people:
>
> www.standard.co.uk/olympics/olympic-news/running-on-blades-the-role-of-technology-in-paralympics-8104167.html

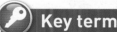 **Key term**

Amputee A person who has lost a limb.

Figure 6.14 Long-handled putters have now been banned from golf

Impact of technology

Has the technology addressed the issues it sought to?

The Rugby Championship – a major international rugby union competition contested annually by Argentina, Australia, New Zealand and South Africa – is owned and managed by SANZAAR. In July 2018, SANZAAR declared that TMO is not working as it should be. It suggested that the system was:

- unfair on players, due to substandard decisions being made
- unfair on officials during game play, due to being wrongly undermined
- unfair on spectators, who are waiting too long for decisions that are often incorrect.

Figure 6.16 Should rugby referees, players and spectators have to wait so long for TMO decisions to be given during game play?

Has the technology had unintended positive and/or negative consequences?

Technological developments occasionally result in unforeseen positive or negative consequences. It can be argued that VAR in football has reduced the incidences of players harassing referees, as they know that decisions have been vetted and checked.

However, one negative example is that of Great Britain Cycling Team's Cervélo velodrome bike, which received some negative press after the 2016 Olympics. The credibility of Great Britain Cycling Team's overall preparations and equipment, including the bike, was questioned by many other competing teams. It was inferred that unfair means might have been used.

Classroom discussion

As a class, you may wish to debate any of the following questions on whether a new technology has done what it intended to or not:

- Has VAR stopped poor decisions in football by referees?
- Has TMO stopped tries being given in rugby? Which ones should not have been given?
- Has Hawk-Eye prevented poor line calls being made in tennis?
- Have running blades allowed amputees to compete on a fair and **level playing field**?

Key term

Level playing field When conditions are the same for all competing.

Read about it

Were Great Britain Cycling Team's rivals right to question how fair it was competing against them?
www.theguardian.com/sport/2016/aug/17/team-gb-cycling-olympic-rivals-question-success-rio-2016

Have developments and adaptations been made to the technology?

Originally invented for cricket, Hawk-Eye was first used in tennis in 2006 and has since been adapted for sports such as football and hurling. In football, it has been adapted to act as goal-line technology.

Similarly, carbon fibre as a material has been adapted for use in many different pieces of sporting equipment, including tennis rackets, golf clubs, bicycles and bobsleighs.

Technology is ever changing and more advances and adaptations are likely to take place in the coming years. It is expected that Wi-Fi connections in stadia will be improved, allowing spectators to choose to watch sport from different perspectives at the touch of a button, for example player's eye view.

Has the technology required developments and adaptations to the sport?

The advent of technology in sport has inadvertently changed the nature of sport forever. One particular example is how tactics and strategies can be employed by performers and coaches to make the most of the technology available. Some examples are given below:

- Formula One teams receive data from their cars that they can act on to decide when to change tyres.
- Tennis players occasionally use the 'challenges' available to them to disrupt play, provide a rest or unsettle their opponent.
- Cricketers may call for a review at a time that suits them for tactical reasons: to unsettle a batsman or to interrupt the flow of the game.
- All decision-based technology – for example TMO, VAR and DRS – has changed the nature of the game, as time has to be taken to review the decisions.

One thing is for certain, amateur performers do not have access to the same technology as elite performers, so it can be argued that the nature of amateur sport is now very different to elite sport.

Are there implications for the future?

In evaluating the impact that technology has had on sport, you may wish to consider if there will be implications for the future.

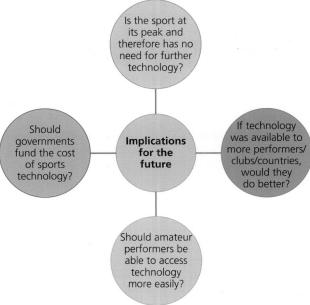

Figure 6.17 Implications for the future

If we use the example of golf clubs, will there need to be a limit as to how much technology is put into developing new clubs? For example, will all golfers be able to hit a golf ball so far that the standard par (the number of shots you should take) for courses will need to be changed? Is there an argument that golf balls made by different companies should follow one particular design that is harder to hit further?

Stretch activity

Produce a 'user guide' to any technological development in sport. Use the following titles to inform the user:

- how the technology works
- for whom it is beneficial and why
- who may disagree with its use and why
- an overall star rating out of five, with justification for the score given.

Know it!

1 State who has been most impacted by an example of technology in a sport of your choice.

2 Using examples, describe how performers have been impacted by technology. Justify your response by referring to whether the technology has been successful for performers.

3 State three examples of how technology has positively affected officials in game play.

4 Describe how you feel one example of sports technology will develop in future years.

Read about it

Restricting the length that a golf ball can be struck:
www.golf.com/tour-news/2017/06/27/time-has-come-restricted-flight-ball-majors

Classroom discussion

Prepare a case for discussion as to why one example of technology in sport has had a greater impact than another.

Group activity

For a specific aspect of sports technology, start to formulate an overall conclusion – has it had a suitable, intended impact? How can you justify your conclusion?

Links to other units

You can find further information on this topic in Units R042, R043, R044 and R045.

Assessment preparation

Think about the tasks that your teacher may set you to assess your ability to evaluate the impact of technology in sport. Make sure you:

- know what aspect of technology you are evaluating
- are clear about what is meant by:
  - impact
  - stakeholders
  - performers, game play and spectators
  - evaluation.

How will you demonstrate that you have made an overall judgement about the impact of a technology, who has been affected, and whether or not it has been applied or adapted to other sports?

Mark scheme

LO4: Be able to evaluate the impact of technology in sport		
Mark band 1	Mark band 2	Mark band 3
Evaluation of the impact of technology in sports in the chosen area is **basic**. **Outlines** the use of the technology being evaluated; consideration of factors affecting its use is **superficial**. There is **minimal** discussion of the impacts that the technology has had. There is **little attempt** to make an overall judgement about whether the technology has succeeded in achieving its aims, enhanced particular aspects of the sport(s) it has been applied to or adapted for other useful means.	Evaluation of the impact of technology in sports in the chosen area is **detailed**. **Describes** the use of the technology being evaluated and **some** factors affecting its use are considered. There is **some relevant** discussion of the impacts that the technology has had. An overall **judgement is made** about whether the technology has succeeded in achieving its aims, enhanced particular aspects of the sport(s) it has been applied to or adapted for other useful means.	Evaluation of the impact of technology in sport in the chosen area is **comprehensive**. **Describes** the use of the technology being evaluated and considers factors affecting its use **in detail**. There is **thorough** discussion of the impacts that the technology has had. An overall **judgement is made and justified** about whether the technology has succeeded in achieving its aims, enhanced particular aspects of the sport(s) it has been applied to or adapted for other useful means.

Glossary

Abdominals Stomach muscles that protect internal organs.

Abduction Moving a limb away from the midline of the body.

Abrasion Surface damage to the skin – cuts and grazes.

Achievement motivation How motivated a performer is to achieve, or their desire to succeed.

Acute injuries Injuries caused by sudden trauma.

Adaptability Flexibility to adapt a programme if, for any reason, the session being performed cannot be followed precisely.

Adduction Bringing a limb towards the midline of the body.

Aerobic exercise Using oxygen to produce energy during low-intensity, long-duration exercise.

Aerobic With oxygen.

Aggression The intention to cause harm to others.

Agility The ability to move and change direction quickly while maintaining control.

Alveoli Tiny air sacs in the lungs.

Amino acids Breakdown product of proteins.

Amputee A person who has lost a limb.

Anaerobic exercise Not using oxygen to produce energy during high-intensity, short-duration exercise.

Anaerobic Without oxygen.

Analytical technology Technology that allows performance and/or physiological measures within the body to be recorded and evaluated.

Anorexia Eating disorder in which people eat too little.

Anxiety A negative emotional state of worry or nervousness.

Application (of technology) How the technology is actually put into use.

Aquatic therapy Fluid environment that adjusts the pressure and resistance on an athlete to assist with recovery and rehabilitation.

Arousal The physiological and psychological activation level of a performer, ranging from being in a coma to high excitement.

Arteries Thick muscular blood vessels that carry blood away from heart.

Arthritis Painful inflammation and stiffness of the joints.

Asthma Lung condition that causes occasional breathing difficulties.

Atria Upper chambers of the heart that collect blood from veins.

Balance The ability to maintain a position; this often involves maintaining the centre of mass over the base of support.

Ball and socket joint Ball-shaped end of bone fits into the socket of another, for example the hip.

Basal metabolic rate (BMR) How quickly an individual uses energy.

Biceps Muscle at the front of the upper arm, which bends the elbow.

Blade Artificial part of a limb made from carbon fibre.

Blisters Bubbles of fluid under the skin caused by friction.

Bradycardia Decrease in the resting heart rate because of training.

Breathing control Exaggerating breaths in and/or out to regain focus.

Burpee A squat thrust and jump.

Calories Units of energy (in nutrition, the energy people get from the food and drink they consume).

Capillaries Tiny, thin blood vessels that join arteries and veins; site of gaseous exchange.

Carbohydrate loading Managing the diet to increase glycogen stores.

Carbohydrates Main source of energy.

Carbon fibre A composite material with a high strength-to-weight ratio.

Cardiac output Amount of blood leaving the heart per minute.

Cardiovascular endurance The ability of the heart, lungs and blood vessels to get oxygen to the muscles and the ability of the body to use that oxygen.

Carpals Bones in the wrist.

Cartilage Flexible tissue; forms padding at ends of long bones; forms ears.

Challenge decisions Decisions in sport that can be challenged as part of the rules or regulations.

Chronic injuries Injuries caused by continuous stress.

Circuit Form of training in which the performer carries out different exercises at various work stations.

Circumduction Conical movement of an extended limb.

Clavicle The collar bone.

Client progress review An interview used to set goals and re-evaluate if any changes need to be made.

Closed fracture Broken bone with no break in the skin.

Concentric Muscle shortens while contracting.

Concussion Injury in which the brain is shaken inside the skull.

Condyloid joint Where curved end of one bone fits against another curved end, for example at the wrist.

Connective tissue White tissue providing support.

Contact sports Sports in which physical contact between performers is an accepted part of play.

Continuous training Any activity or exercise that can be continuously repeated without suffering undue fatigue.

Contusion Bruise.

Cool down Easy exercise done after more intense exercise to allow the body to recover to resting levels.

Core muscles Muscles of the trunk.

Cramp Involuntary contraction of muscle.

Cranium Skull bone surrounding and protecting the brain.

Creatine Dietary supplements containing creatine phosphate.

Dehydration Harmful reduction in the amount of water in the body.

Deltoids Muscles on shoulder joint that move the upper arm.

Diabetes Condition in which blood sugar levels are unregulated by the body.

Diaphragm Muscle causing inhalation.

Diastolic blood pressure Blood pressure when the heart is relaxed.

Direct aggression Any act that is directed at an opponent, performer or official with the intention of hurting them.

Drag The resistant force that water exerts against the body.

Dynamic stretching A stretch that takes the body through the range of motion but is not held for any length of time.

Eccentric Muscle lengthens while contracting.

Emergency action plan (EAP) Written document identifying what action to take in the event of an emergency at a sporting event.

Emergency communication Details of whom to contact in an emergency.

Emergency equipment Equipment required in an emergency situation, for example first-aid kits, stretchers and defibrillators.

Emergency personnel People who are responsible in an emergency, such as first responders and qualified first aiders.

Endurance/aerobic activities Low-intensity, long-duration activities.

Epilepsy Condition causing abnormal brain activity leading to seizures.

Exhalation Breathing out.

Extension Movement when angle between bones increases (straightening).

Extrinsic factors Risks or factors from outside the body.

Extrinsic motivation The drive from a performer to achieve a tangible or intangible reward; it comes from a source external to the performer.

Extrovert Personality type characterised by being sociable, outgoing, talkative, needing high arousal levels and prone to boredom; extroverts tend to perform team sports.

Fartlek training 'Speed play', which generally involves running, combining continuous and interval training.

Fats Source of energy and vitamins.

Fatty acids Breakdown product of fats.

Femur Bone of the thigh or upper leg, which extends from the hip to the knee.

Fibre Roughage helps prevent constipation.

Fibula Bone in the lower leg that forms the ankle.

Fitness Set of qualities relating to a person's ability to perform physical activity.

FITTA Principles of overload: frequency, intensity, time, type, adherence.

Flexibility The ability to move joints through a large range of motion; the range of movement around a joint.

Flexion Movement when angle between bones decreases (bending).

Food allergy A reaction of the immune system to certain foods that it mistakenly perceives as a threat.

Food intolerance Being unable to digest certain types of food.

Fracture Partial or complete break in a bone.

Gait How people walk or run.

Gastrocnemius and soleus The calf muscles used to push the foot off the ground when running.

Gliding joint Where one bone can slide over another, for example the carpals in the wrist.

Gluteals Buttock muscles, which are used when running.

Golfer's elbow Tendon injury due to repetitive actions such as golf strokes.

Hamstrings Muscles at the back of the upper leg; they bend the knee.

Hazard Something that can cause harm.

Heart disease Build-up of fatty deposits in the coronary arteries that limits the supply of blood to the heart, leading to a heart attack.

Heart rate Number of times the heart contracts per minute.

Heat exhaustion Fatigue and collapse resulting from prolonged exposure to excessive or unaccustomed heat.

Heat treatment Use of heat to reduce pain and stiffness, and to speed up healing.

Heatstroke Failure of the body's temperature-regulating mechanism when subjected to excessively high temperatures; it can result in fever and unconsciousness.

Herbal remedies Dietary supplements derived from plants for medicinal purposes.

Hinge joint Where one end of one bone fits against another bone allowing movement in only one direction, for example the knee.

Humerus Bone in the upper arm.

Hydration Taking on fluids.

Hyperbaric chamber Medical treatment in which you breathe pure oxygen inside a highly pressured chamber; it accelerates the body's natural healing process from injury or disease.

Hypertrophy An increase in muscle size as a result of training.

Hypothermia A dangerous drop in body temperature.

Ice therapy Use of ice to reduce pain and swelling.

Imagery Where a performer pictures something in their head to try to maintain focus.

Indirect aggression When an act of frustration is aggressively directed at a sporting object.

Inhalation Breathing in.

Insulin-dependent diabetes Type 1 diabetes; requires insulin injections.

Insulin-resistant diabetes Type 2 diabetes; usually managed through careful dietary control.

Interval training Any training that involves periods of work and rest.

Intrinsic factors Risks or factors from within the body.

Intrinsic motivation Comes from within a performer; the internal drive to achieve something.

Introvert Personality type characterised by shyness, concentration, thoughtfulness and low arousal levels; introverts tend to perform individual sports.

Isometric Muscle contracts but no movement.

Isotonic Muscle contracts and movement occurs.

Kyphosis Excessive backward or outward curvature of the upper part of the spine.

Lactic acid Waste product of anaerobic exercise; it causes fatigue.

Latissimus dorsi Muscle at the side of back that moves the upper arm.

Level playing field When conditions are the same for all competing.

Ligaments Fibrous bands that join bone to bone to strengthen joints.

Lordosis Excessive forward or inward curving of the lower back.

Lung capacity Amount of air your lungs can hold.

Lungs Large spongy organs in chest; used for gas exchange.

Macronutrients Nutrients that provide energy, which are needed in the largest amounts in our diet – carbohydrates fats and proteins.

Malnutrition Condition that occurs when a person's diet does not contain the right amount of nutrients.

Marginal gains Small, incremental improvements in any process.

Maximal tests Fitness tests that require maximal effort in order to produce a valid, comparable result.

Mechanical assistance The use of devices or equipment to guide and support a performer when performing a skill.

Mental rehearsal Visualising or imagining each aspect of an activity before performing it.

Metacarpals Bones in the palm of the hand.

Metatarsals Bones in the foot.

Micronutrients Nutrients needed in small amounts in our diet that are required for healthy growth and development – vitamins and minerals.

Moderation Taking individual characteristics and circumstances into consideration when designing a training programme.

Motion tracking software Technology that tracks the movement and distance covered by a performer.

Motivation The drive or desire to achieve something.

Multi-vitamins Dietary supplements containing vitamins.

Muscle imbalance Where one muscle is more powerful than an opposing one.

Muscular endurance Ability of muscles to keep contracting repeatedly.

Muscular strength The ability of a muscle or group of muscles to exert force.

Need to achieve (NACH) Personality that wants to win, accepts challenges and competition, and persists in the face of failure.

Need to avoid failure (NAF) Personality that is afraid of evaluation when losing or failing, so often avoids competitive, challenging circumstances.

Non-contact sports Sports where participants compete alternately, or in lanes, so that they are physically separated, or where the rules detail no contact.

Normative data Data from a reference population that establishes a baseline score or measurement, and against which your score or measurement can be compared.

Nutrients Substances in food needed for our bodies to function.

Obesity The state of being very overweight; where more than 40 per cent of body mass is fat.

Objective data Facts and numbers that can be measured.

Open fracture Broken bone in which the skin is also broken, exposing the bone.

Optimal level (of arousal) The perfect level of arousal for the task being done.

Osgood-Schlatter's disease Knee pain caused by growth spurts.

Osteoporosis Weakening of bones in older people.

Overload Working harder than normal.

Overnutrition Condition caused by excess nutrients in the diet.

Over-reliance on technology When performers rely on technology to make up for their lack of skill.

Overtraining Training too hard/often; not giving body time to fully recover.

Overuse injuries Chronic injuries caused by repetitive movements.

PAR-Q Physical activity readiness questionnaire – an introductory 'yes/no' questionnaire that aims to identify the small number of people for whom physical activity might be unsuitable on the grounds of medical advice.

Patella The knee cap; covers the knee joint.

Pectorals Muscles in the chest that move the upper arm.

Pelvic girdle Also called the pelvis; attached to backbone; forms hip joint with femur.

Pelvis Large bone attached to the backbone and forming the hip joint with the legs.

Personality The total number of unique characteristics of a person that distinguish them from other people, forming their character.

Pivot joint Where the round end on one bone fits into a ring formed by another, for example the vertebrae of the next, which allow head rotation.

Plasma Fluid part of the blood that transports blood celles and dissolved nutrients.

Platelets Component of the blood involved in blood clotting.

Plyometric training Repeated exercises such as bounding, hopping or jumping over hurdles to designed to create fast, powerful movements.

Posture Position the body is held in.

Power Exerting muscular strength rapidly.

Pre-exercise meal Planned food intake three to four hours before exercise.

Progressive overload Gradually making training harder as it becomes too easy.

Protective clothing Clothing designed to prevent injury in sport.

Protein powders Dietary supplements containing additional protein.

Proteins Needed for growth and repair.

Psychological factors Mental factors that can affect a performer positively or negatively.

Quadriceps Muscles at the front of the upper leg that straighten the leg.

Questionnaire A series of questions to be answered truthfully.

Radius Bone of the forearm; attaches to the thumb side of the wrist.

Red blood cells Component of the blood involved in transporting oxygen and carbon dioxide.

Rehydrate Replace lost fluids.

Releasing tension in muscles A mixture of deep breathing and the slow release of tense muscles.

Reliability A fitness test is reliable if it can be repeated and gives similar results each time.

Resistance training Training that involves working against some kind of force that 'resists' your movement.

Reversibility/regression 'Use it or lose it' – if you stop training, you will lose fitness.

Ribs Bones surrounding the heart and lungs, forming the chest cavity.

RICE Acronym for rest, ice, compression and elevation – the treatment for soft tissue injuries.

Risk The likelihood of a hazard causing harm.

Risk assessment Careful examination of what, in relation to a sports activity, could cause harm to people and trying to minimise the risk of harm occurring.

Rotation Turning part of body around its axis.

Saddle joint Where a saddle-shaped bone fits on another, for example in the thumb.

SALTAPS Acronym for see, ask, look, touch, active, passive and strength.

Scapula The shoulder blade.

SCAT Sport competition anxiety test.

Scoliosis Condition where the spine is visibly curved to the side, giving a 'S' or 'C' shape.

Sever's disease Heel pain caused by an inflamed growth plate.

Shin splints Pain in the shins or the front of the lower legs; usually caused by exercise.

Shock zone Area of the foot that impacts with the ground when running.

Simulators Technology that allows you simulate the real-world action and outcome of a sporting skill in an artificial environment.

Sling Support, usually of folded cloth, to immobilise and rest the injured limb.

Slouching Standing, moving or sitting in a lazy, drooping way.

SMART Goals that are specific, measurable, achievable, realistic and time-bound.

Social learning theory A theory about how we develop our personality by watching and copying others.

Social media Computer-based technologies that facilitate the creation and sharing of information and ideas via virtual communities and networks, for example Twitter, Facebook and Instagram.

Soft tissue injuries Damage to muscles, ligaments or tendons.

Specificity Making training suited to the movements, skills and muscles that are used in an activity.

Spectatorship Those watching at the sporting event, on the move or at home.

Splint Plastic or fibreglass support for limb fractures and sprains.

Sprains Injuries to ligaments.

STAI State anxiety inventory test.

Stakeholders in sport Athletes/performers, spectators, professional bodies.

Static stretching Holding stretches, either actively or passively, to increase the range of movement at a joint.

Sternum The breast bone.

Strains Injuries to muscles.

Strength endurance Ability to apply strength in activities that have an element of endurance (a long duration).

Strength The extent to which a muscle or muscle group can contract against resistance.

Stress Emotional strain or tension.

Stroke A life-threatening medical condition caused by a lack of blood supply to part of the brain.

Stroke volume Amount of blood leaving the heart with each beat.

Subjective data Opinions and thoughts.

Sub-maximal tests Fitness tests that do not require maximal exertion.

Synovial joint A freely moveable joint.

Systolic blood pressure Blood pressure when the heart is contracting.

Tarsals Bones in the foot that form the ankle joint.

Technology Putting scientific knowledge into practical use to solve problems or invent useful tools.

Technology doping The practice of gaining competitive advantage using high-tech sports equipment.

Tendonitis Chronic injury to tendons.

Tendons Join muscles to bone.

Tennis elbow Tendon injury due to repetitive actions such as tennis strokes.

Tibia The shin bone; forms knee joint with the femur.

Tidal volume Amount of air you breathe in and out at rest.

Trachea Tube connecting the mouth and nose to the lungs.

Traditional nature of the sport The standard ways and rules that have been used in a sport for a number of years.

Training The process of bringing a person to a suitable level of proficiency.

Traits Distinguishing characteristics that typically belong to a person, which make up their personality.

Trapezius Muscle at the top of the back that moves the scapula and head.

Triceps Muscle at the back of the upper arm, which straightens the elbow.

Ulna Bone of the forearm; forms the point of the elbow.

Umpire decision review system (DRS) Technology-based system used in cricket to review controversial decisions made by the on-field umpires as to whether or not a batsman had been dismissed.

Undernutrition Condition caused by insufficient nutrients in the diet.

Validity A fitness test is valid if it tests the component of fitness that it aims to test.

Valves Prevent the backflow of blood in the heart.

Variance Altering and changing elements of training in order to prevent boredom.

Vascular shunt mechanism Mechanism that changes the size of arteries to move blood to where it is needed most.

Veins Thin-walled blood vessels returning blood to the heart; they have one-way valves.

Ventricles Lower chambers of the heart that pump blood out through arteries.

Vertebrae Many single bones joined together to form the backbone.

Viscous Thick, sticky consistency.

Visual representation A method of showing something that can be seen.

Vital capacity Amount of air expelled from your lungs when you take a deep breath and then exhale fully.

Vitamins and minerals Substances needed for many essential functions of the body.

Vomiting Being sick/throwing up.

Warm up A simple exercise routine performed before a training session.

Water Good hydration is vital for reactions, lubrication and temperature regulation.

White blood cells Component of the blood involved in fighting infection.

Work-to-rest ratio The amount of exercise (work) compared to the amount of rest.

Zone of optimal functioning A zone of arousal that is optimal for what the performer is doing.

Index